*The Rope Carrier*

*Theresa Tomlinson*

# The Rope Carrier

JM Julia MacRae Books

LONDON SYDNEY AUCKLAND JOHANNESBURG

First published in Great Britain 1991
by Julia MacRae
an imprint of the Random Century Group
20 Vauxhall Bridge Road, London SW1V 2SA

Random Century Australia (Pty) Ltd
20 Alfred Street, Milsons Point, Sydney, NSW 2061

Random Century New Zealand Ltd,
PO Box 40-086, Glenfield, Auckland 10, New Zealand

Random Century South Africa (Pty) Ltd
PO Box 337, Bergvlei, 2012, South Africa

Typeset by Falcon Typographic Art Ltd
Edinburgh and London
Printed and bound in Great Britain by
Bookcraft (Bath) Ltd

British Library Cataloguing in Publication Data
Tomlinson, Theresa
The rope carrier
I. Title
823.914

ISBN 1-85681-241-3

*For Hilda, Rene, Ann, Jay*
*and all the other Hurlfield Writers*

# Acknowledgements

I would like to thank the following people for their kind help and advice:

The staff of Sheffield Local Studies Library;

Sheila and Bernard Callan, and the Abbeydale Grange Local History Workshop;

John Capes of 'Rare and Racy', Antiquarian Books, Maps and Engravings, Division Street, Sheffield.

# Part One: From the Cave

'In the hollow cavern is a whole subterannean village.'

*Moritz's Travels*, 1782.

'Now to the cave, we come, wherein is found,
A new strange thing, a village underground:
Houses and barns for men and beasts behoof,
With walls distinct, under one solid roof.'

from *Wonders of the Peak*, 1692, Cotton.

# Chapter One

1786

Water dripped down from the great dark arch of the cavern roof.

'Hold it up, girl. Hold it higher. Remember Great Grandma.'

Minnie Dakin sighed and pushed up the rushlight, holding it steady so that her father could see his work. Her shoulders ached with the effort of keeping the light steady, and her eyes watered as smoke blew into her face each time the wind gusted through the mouth of the cave.

Great Grandma Dakin . . . Minnie was weary of remembering her and what she had said. Grandma's words had plagued her life ever since she could remember.

Minnie had been born on the very day that Great Grandma had died. Minnie's mother Annie had laboured to bring her sixth child into the world in the tiny one-roomed cottage that leant against the side of the cavern wall. Great Grandma had given up the pile of matted straw, covered by a woven rug, that they called with reverence "the bed". She'd insisted on helping with the birth, though she could scarce see her hand in front of her face. She claimed that she had attended more birthings than any other woman in Derbyshire. She could tell just what stage the woman had reached by the sounds that she made and Grandma's clever sense of touch told her strong fingers what to do.

So the baby had been born safely, another girl to add to the three surviving daughters. Annie had looked down at her baby with disappointment, thinking of the family's need for strong healthy workers to make the ropes which they depended on for their living.

'A lad would have been better.'

Great Grandma had sat down beside her on the bed. She'd taken the baby in her arms, and felt carefully at its kicking legs and punching arms. She wrapped the child in a soft woven blanket made from warm oily sheep's wool.

'Nay,' she said. 'This little lass is strong. She will carry the ropes, and walk for ever. Call her Minerva and she shall be a spinner.'

Then Great Grandma had bowed her head over the baby, and died.

That was how Minnie Dakin had been born, and how her mother had gained an almost magical faith in her daughter's strength and cleverness. That was why the nine-year-old Minnie came to be standing beside her father, holding the rushlight while he made whiplashes for four-in-hand coaches. It was close to midnight on a wild winter's night, for he kept the secrets of his craft by working in the darkness.

Minnie twisted her head to look at the gentle oil-lamp glow that came from the hut her father had built for the three remaining girls to sleep in. Sarah, the eldest, had married one of the lead miners and gone to live in his parents' cottage in the village, where she struggled to bring up her six little ones, dreading the fast-coming day when her five-year-old son should be sent to work at the mine, washing and sorting the ore. Sarah thought that she had gone up in the world, now that she was living in a proper stone-built cottage, out in the daylight, but Minnie couldn't see why.

Here in the cave, space was plentiful, and there was no rent to pay. The building of an extra room was a matter of a few days' labour. She loved the warm bed which she shared with her sisters, and now she longed to climb in between their fat sweating bodies and settle down to sleep, with her nose tucked into the hair at the nape of Netty's neck and Sally's arms around her.

Lazy cows they are, thought Minnie. A faint rippling sound from the deep dark tunnel at the back of the cave lifted the hairs on the back of her neck.

'Whisht child! Hold still, will you? What is it?'

Minnie stared silent and large-eyed at her father.

'Oh, Minnie. It's not the devil's laughter again?'

A touch of ice ran from the back of her head down to her heels, as though a drop of water from the constantly dripping roof had trickled down her neck. Minnie shuddered, and moved to one side. She often felt that freezing touch when she was up late at night helping her father. She braced herself and tried to turn her attention to the work that he was doing. She must try to remember the sequence of twists and skilful knots that his hard leather-skinned fingers made. She should not feel cold and there was no reason to be afraid, so she told herself. She had been born into this darkness and had known nothing else but the cool, damp atmosphere that stayed the same through summer and winter, through night and day. But at times like this, Minnie found that the stories told by Marcus the weaver came creeping into her mind. Stories from long-ago about the terrifying robber chief who'd held a great feast, there in the deepest caverns, and had invited the devil to come.

Minnie shuddered and forced herself to think about the other story that Marcus told. It was just as old, so Marcus said, and perhaps it was even true.

Minnie could picture him now, the young shepherd boy who'd seen one of his sheep straying into the mouth of the cave and followed him in. Further and further he'd gone, deep into the heart of the earth, following the patter of small hoofed feet. Then he'd come to the lowest of openings, he'd found sheep droppings. . . so, being very thin and small himself, he'd wriggled through after his sheep. Beyond the tunnel he had found a magical cavern, lit from within, where waterfalls splashed crystal-clear water over the rocks and lovely flowers bloomed. Then the shepherd stepped out into a land of wide fields full of rippling golden corn and cheerful reapers cutting it, bringing in a plentiful harvest.

The shepherd boy had returned with his sheep and told everyone of the wonderful place that he'd found, but when he'd tried to show them where it was, he couldn't find the tiny secret entrance.

'Of course,' said Marcus, 'they all thought that he had made it up, to make himself important,' and perhaps that was true, but Minnie loved the story, and she believed in the shepherd boy for he had the power to banish the devil's laughter. And, after all, Marcus had said that the shepherd boy continued to search for the passageway long after everyone else had lost interest and laughed him to scorn. Even when he was old and white-haired, still he searched on alone.

At last John Dakin finished his task and piled the cut ends of hemp into his bag. He gave Minnie the nod to climb up the side of the ropewalk ahead of him, lighting his steps back to the cobbled stone huts that were their homes.

## Chapter Two

Minnie rolled over and groaned, fishing around by her feet for the blanket that her sisters had thrown off as they struggled out of the bed.

'Shift thee'sen, lazy bones.' Sally's strong snappy fingers came creeping under the cover and pinched Minnie hard on the backside.

'Leave me be, thee great fat sow.' Minnie pulled herself up, red-faced, nostrils flaring, steely-grey eyes wide open, glittering in the candlelight.

'Skinny rat, skinny rat.' Sally bent down and grabbed Minnie by the ankles, pulling her to the edge of the bed, tickling her in the ribs. Minnie kicked back at her face.

'Leave be, the pair of you, and get yourselves sorted out, or we'll all be feeling the flat of mother's hand.' Netty punched at them both, but it didn't hurt. Netty's punches never hurt.

Both Minnie's sisters were strong, well-built girls, plump in all the right places. It was all the fashion to be fat like that and Minnie hated them for it. Netty was sixteen, and she was kind. Sally was fourteen, and she wasn't. Minnie was nine years old, skinny, and small for her age, but she was strong too, in her own determined, wiry way.

Netty grabbed Sally by the arm and pulled her through the door hole, holding aside the woven curtain that served as a door.

ropewalk ready for the light.'

Minnie crept back into the bed, pulling the blanket over her
head, trying to sleep again, but suddenly Annie's voice was
calling out, 'Minnie, Minnie. Are you up, my darling?'
    Then came the rattle of the wooden bowls being set out
on the window-sill. Minnie dragged herself to the edge of the
mattress and began pulling her woollen bedgown on over her
petticoat and fastening her apron over the top to keep it fixed.
She grumbled and growled to herself at the stupidity of calling
it a bedgown when it was what you put on to go out in, and at
the dreadful unfairness of having to be up in the morning when
you'd been working at night while others were sleeping.
    'Minnie, Minnie. Are you up, child?'
    Minnie sighed, and reached for her cloak. She wrapped it
tight round her shoulders and fastened it at the front.
    'Minnie, Minnie. Fetch the water will you, child, and some

more sticks for the fire. Come on, my lass, there'll be no porridge for anyone until you've done.'

Minnie emerged yawning from behind the curtain and went to lift the earthenware pitcher.

'Some folks were up late last night. Some folks were working while others slept. Some folk might be weary.'

Her mother smiled as she shoved the spinning wheel out in front of the cottage and turned to fetch her stool.

'Ah, well, some might I daresay, but not my Minnie, not my darling girl.'

'Huh!' Minnie hunched up her shoulders and carried the pitcher down the path between the cottages, past the ropewalks to the river. She lowered the pitcher into the water that ran fast and clear and ice-cold through the cave. As she turned back and climbed up through the ropewalks and then past the cottages, there was noise and busyness on both sides. Fires were stoked and the clatter of pans rang out. Soot and smoke puthered out of chimneys, up towards the roof of the cavern, as long fingers of grey light came creeping inside from the round eye of the entrance.

Her sisters were already starting their work on the top Dakin terrace. Netty had fastened a twist of hemp to one of the hooks on the spinning wheel, and she was beginning the long backwards walk, pulling out the hemp from the bundle that she'd fastened around her waist. She had to stop and shout at Sally to get her to pay attention and turn the wheel steady, instead of flashing her eyes and calling out to the Whittingham lads who were beginning their work two terraces below.

Minnie thumped the pitcher down beside Annie's cooking pot.

'Whoops, sorry,' she muttered as the water slopped over the top.

'I'll give you sorry,' Annie grinned, threatening to clout

her ears. 'Now off you go and fetch me fresh sticks to set in the stack to dry. A great armful I want to see. Arms so full they're breaking. Off with you.'

Minnie blinked and yawned when the bright morning light hit her face as she emerged from the cave and onto the pathway, with the fast river running along beside it. She put up her hand, shading her eyes as she turned to look along the steep sides of the ravine and up at the ruined castle perched high on the top, as she did every morning.

'Yah,' she yelled, startling and scattering the rooks who nested on the trees that grew out sideways from the steep rockside. Then, giggling at their fright, she set off to cross the small bridge into Castleton village and climb up the wooded hillside where the best small firewood sticks could be found.

When Minnie returned, so laden with sticks that they would keep dropping, she found a young man in good clothes standing at the end of the pathway, looking up at the great archway that led into the cave.

Minnie had seen others standing there before, with the same expression on their faces. The man stared up at the great opening with dread and suspicion. Tall wooden posts stood in front of the cave. Small crossbars and supports were nailed over the tops, giving the posts the look of spindly gibbets. Gibbets for cats, they'd have to be.

'Stretching posts they are,' Minnie told him. 'See the ropes slung over them, weighted with those stones? Gives our ropes a good stretch that does. Our ropes will last for ever, so my father says.'

'Ah.' The young man nodded his understanding and stood back to let Minnie pass.

Rich visitors often came to wonder at the marvels of the cave. Sometimes they spoke in loud disgusted voices, calling the cottages "hovels" and passing rude remarks about the rope

makers' living conditions. Annie was always quick to reply
that they'd fresh air, clean water, plenty of space and the
constant plodding exercise of the ropewalks. She'd tell how
the Whittinghams and the Dakins and the Marrisons all had
folk who'd lived to be very old, and never stopped work till
the day they died.

'In this cave,' Annie would say, 'if you live to be five, you'll
live for ever.'

The young man touched Minnie's arm as she passed him.
'Er, can you help me, missy? I'm looking for a guide.'

'Oh, aye. My sisters can do that.'

'Your sisters?'

'Yes, sir. Grand guides my sisters are. You come inside and
speak to my father.'

The man hesitated for a moment, then followed her. He
touched her arm again.

'Here, let me carry tha sticks.'

Minnie smiled and looked at him again. 'You'll get your fine clothes all messed up.'

'Not my clothes,' he said, 'my master's clothes, though I wear them. Only mine until next hiring fair.'

He hesitated again, then stopped. The fear had come back into his eyes. ''Tis not for me this guide I'm after, 'tis for my master. I would not wish to enter such a God-forsaken hole as this.'

Minnie laughed, somehow feeling cheeky and confident with this ignorant young man. 'Come on. Come a little further. There now, look.'

The man moved forward, then stopped again. His mouth dropped open as he saw the cottages and the ropewalks, and little Maud Whittingham come charging along with the pig that they shared with the Dakin family. Minnie's sisters were well into their work now, moving faster to warm themselves.

'See,' said Minnie. 'There's nowt to be afraid of.'

'Why, 'tis like a little underground town.'

'Aye, that it is. That's Dame Whittingham's, she brews fine ale and runs the inn. And that's Marcus the weaver, just setting up his loom. We have all we need in here, and a lot more besides. Tell me your name, sir, and I'll fetch my father to you.' She winked and smiled the way she'd seen Netty and Sally do, for she liked the look of him.

'Josh. Joshua Eyre.'

'Ah well, Mr Joshua Eyre, will you please follow me, and stop that peeking at my sisters.'

She thumbed her nose at him and led the way to their cottage, shouting to her father to come and see the gentleman, giggling at his embarrassment, forgetting completely that she'd heard the devil's laughter in the night.

# Chapter Three

John Dakin stuck his head out from behind the curtain that covered the cottage doorway. He guessed the purpose of this young man's visit and reappeared pulling on his woollen waistcoat.

''Tis a guide you're looking for?'

'Aye, for my master, Dr Frazer, from Sheffield.'

'Well? When does your master wish to visit?'

The young man seemed not to hear.

'Oh . . . I beg pardon, sir. What did you say?'

Minnie clapped her hand to her mouth to cover her giggles, for it was clear that the man could not take his eyes from the ropewalk where Netty made her return journey, round strong hips swaying in a steady walking rhythm, holding the rope yarn at tension, while Sally talked ten to the dozen to Ben Whittingham as she wound the rope onto the reel.

John Dakin smiled, and repeated his question. He was used to the distracted looks of those who stepped inside the cave for the first time.

'Pardon, sir. Dr Frazer wishes to visit the cave today if that's convenient to thee. He's staying at the Castle Inn, but he must return to Sheffield tomorrow.'

The arrangements were made and the young man strode out into the bright daylight again, giving many a surprised and puzzled glance back behind him. Minnie was sent to help her mother dish out the porridge.

'Did he ask for singers?' Mrs Dakin demanded.

Minnie pulled a face. 'He did not.'

'Never you mind with your sour face, my lass. Singers is what he'll get, or rather, one sweet angel singer is what he'll get, and that will be my little Minnie, for I can't spare Sally as well as Netty. Now call them in to sup, then set yourself to carding that basket of hemp and practise your warbling, my love. If he pays well there may be a farthing coming to my Minnie.'

Minnie wrinkled up her nose but she knew better than to disobey her mother, so she called in the girls. Then, pulling her cloak tight around her, she lowered herself down onto a tuffet of rotting straw that was heaped beside the basket of raw hemp. She picked up the carding comb and worked away fast, trying to get herself warm. She sang out loud and raucous,

'Oh, the ram was fat in front, sir,
The ram was fat on top,
The ram was fat behind, si . . .ir –'

Her mother stuck her head out of the window hole. 'Like an angel. Like an *angel*, I said.'

Minnie stopped for a moment, comb in the air, then began,

'The cuckoo is a pretty bird.
Sing cuckoo, sing cuckoo.'

The young man returned with his master, a fat-bellied man dressed in a black frock-coat with a high collar and expensive pearl buttons that only just fastened around him; they looked as though they might pop at any moment. His legs were skinny sticks, and Minnie wondered how they could manage to hold up his great round body. The fashionable shoes that enclosed his small feet were the buckled type, dainty as any lady's, and altogether unsuitable for exploring the deep tunnels. The Dakin family stared down at such fine footwear, but nothing was said.

'This is my daughter, Netty,' said Mr Dakin. 'I'd take you myself, but there's some rope needed urgent for one of the mines and I must get it finished. Our Netty is as good a guide as any you'll find.'

Dr Frazer looked surprised, but grunted his approval as Netty dropped him a curtsey and turned to lead the way down to the river that ran through the cave.

'There's only one way through to the great cave, sir, and that's along the river. You must get into the boat, sir, and you must lie down on your back, if you please. Fetch the candles, Minnie.'

When Minnie returned with the lighted candles, she found the gentleman lying in the straw in the bottom of the boat, his mountainous stomach almost touching the roof of the tunnel. His shaved head bare, he clutched his powdered wig across his chest. Terror showed on his face.

'Is there no other way but this?'

'There's no other way, sir,' Netty replied. 'None but a low rocky tunnel, only fit for a child to crawl through, full of rubble and stones, and I fear, sir, you would never get your . . . never get through without ruining your fine coat.'

'Where does this water come from? What river is this?'

'Why they call it Peakshole Water, sir, or sometimes they call it the River Styx.'

'The Styx? But that is the river that runs through hell.'

'Oh yes, sir. They say this is the devil's cave, though we live here comfortably enough. Now, sir, I must ask you to take this lighted candle to hold in your hand. It will light up the roof of the tunnel for you.'

He took the candle, fussing that it might set his wig alight, then ordered his servant to carry the wig for him and not get it wet. Josh took the wig and put it into a leather satchel. Minnie wrinkled her nose; she wondered how rich folk could bear to wear such things, smelling of grease and stale powdered cornflour as it did.

'How is this contraption to be moved?' The doctor's voice squeaked with anxiety.

'Why, sir, I'm to push it,' answered Netty, and she plunged into the water, not even gasping at the cold.

The doctor twisted his head around as best he could without banging it on the roof of the tunnel. Then the manservant plunged in after Netty, though he *did* gasp and shudder at the shock of the water, and took hold of the boat's side.

'Here, let me do the pushing for you.'

'Nay,' said Netty. 'For I'm used to doing it, though I thank thee kindly for the thought.'

'Leave the girl be,' the doctor ordered. 'You take good care to keep my wig dry or it'll be the worst for you.'

So up to their waists in the water, with Netty pushing and

the young man following, they disappeared along the tunnel. Minnie watched them go, then turned to the low opening of the rocky hole. She got down onto her hands and knees and gritted her teeth. At least she could remain dry; it would be trouble enough to sort out Netty's soaked petticoats. She stuck her head into the gravelly tunnel, holding one lighted candle ahead, and weaseled her way forward, grumbling at the sharp stones that grazed her hands and cheeks and cursing at the hot fat that spilled onto her fingers, for she must keep at least one candle alight. At last she had covered the ten-yard crawl and was able to pull herself up. She dusted herself down and prepared for the scramble up the rough cave side that would take her onto the high ledge they called the orchestra.

Quietly she set herself out with three candles lit at her feet, while voices and splashing and, at last, footsteps sounded from below. The lights of Netty's candles appeared down in the dim distance. Minnie waited; waited while the doctor exclaimed at the wonder of the constant stream of water that pattered down from high in the cave. She heard Netty's voice clear and strong.

'We call it Roger Rain's House, sir.'

Then, choosing her moment when all had gone quiet, Minnie took up a candle in each hand and chimed in a sweet high voice, her chin lifted to the roof, moulding her features into a mask of innocence, a face like an angel's,

'The holly and the ivy,
When they are both full grown,
O-of all the trees that are in the wood,
The-e holly bears the crown.'

While she sang, she thought with relish of the farthing that she hoped might come her way.

\*　　\*　　\*

The doctor paid them well and pinched her cheek when he
left. He kept laughing and talking about the dinner that was
being prepared for him at the Castle Inn before he set off on
his journey back to Sheffield. Relief made him jolly. He had
fine stories to tell of his dangerous exploits in the cave, though
Minnie could be sure that he'd never repeat the experience.

Netty stood around in her wet skirts talking to the manservant Josh, though her mother fussed that she should set
her petticoats to dry. Then at last they were gone, and Minnie
was sent to help Sally on the ropewalk while Netty went to
the fire to dry her skirts. Sally snapped and complained at
the way her sister twisted the yarn but Minnie refused to get
angry, for she had a farthing in her pocket.

# Chapter Four

The gruelling winter months came. Icicles dripped from the mouth of the cavern, and the roof and walls ran with water. The ropemakers' fires filled the cave with smuts and thick, choking smoke. The pigs that could not be taken out to graze on the common added to the stench and the mouldering rushes strewn on the damp rock floors grew thick with the filth of human living.

Minnie looked forward to the clean fresh air that her wood-gathering expeditions brought, even when she had to tramp through snow and ice. Sometimes she'd walk further than she really needed to. Then she'd return with raw chilblained fingers and feet, and blinded with tears which the cold brought to her eyes. For a little while then the smelly, smoke-filled, damp recesses of the cave took on a welcoming aspect.

Certainly Minnie had no wish to live in one of the small lead-miners' cottages that filled the small town of Castleton, in higgeldy-piggeldy rows. She often called in on her oldest sister Sarah and took the three middle children back to the cave with her, where they spent the day with Grandma Annie, learning to card the ropemakers' hemp.

Minnie grew sad at the sight of Sarah who was turning into a thin haggard old woman – at the age of twenty-four. She'd had seven children, and six of them had survived, but now that Sarah was expecting her eighth, they were cramped and miserable in the two-roomed cottage that they shared with Matthew's parents. Even though Sarah's eldest lad had started to work at the mine with his father, they still could not afford to rent a second cottage. Sarah dragged herself through the work of the day looking sick and exhausted.

The children loved it when Minnie took them to the cave, for there they had room to skip and play chase. They laughed and ducked away from the quick cuffs and kicks that came from their gran as they scambled around her fire.

Annie would sit at her spinning wheel, shouting orders and instructions to her husband and the girls on the rope-walks below.

'Step out faster,' she would snap back at anyone who had the cheek to complain of the cold. 'Step out faster then, and get those threads turning.'

Sometimes she would start to sing in a strong deep voice, exaggerating the rhythm, and wagging her head in time:

'Spin Sally spin,
Your bread you must win,
Twist the yarn and break it not,
Spin Sally spin.'

She would put into the song the name of the person who had complained. It was usually Sally, but sometimes Minnie; or she would use the name of anyone whom she thought might not quite be pulling their weight. All the other workers would take up the song and laugh and stare at the person named until they blushed for shame and quickened their pace. Sarah's children adored their grandma, and egged her on by pointing out anyone who might be lagging a bit.

Christmas brought some relief from the hardness of life. The gypsies arrived as they did each year at that time, bringing

their wagons and carts to rest under the shelter of the cave and letting their horses loose on the commons that surrounded the village.

Work was set aside for a short time; the cave-dwellers much preferred to listen to the gypsies' news and excitement, their stories and songs. The cave was crowded and noisy with it all. There were feasts and singing and dancing each night.

Queenie Wood was especially welcomed by Annie. The two were almost the same age and had known each other through these annual visits since they were little children. A great deal of hugging and kissing went on at first and then the two women would send Minnie off to Dame Alice's to fetch jugs of ale while they settled themselves by the fire to smoke pipes of tobacco, and talk and laugh long into the night.

Minnie curled herself up close to the fire, quiet and still, like a cat, so they would forget that she was there. She loved listening to Queenie who spoke loud and fast and smelt deliciously of the herbs that she gathered and sold. Queenie could cure a fever, or cramps in the stomach, or even mend a broken heart.

'Aye, Annie, we've seen some strange goings-on lately. They're digging away at the land, making these great long straight rivers. They call them canals.'

'What?' said Annie. 'What the devil are they doing that for?'

'They make 'em so as to carry heavy loads along in boats. Right into the big towns the boats go, all loaded up with I don't know what.'

'They've no business doing that,' Annie insisted. 'Rivers should be where God puts 'em, that's what I say, like our river. God put it here and we use it, that's how it should be.'

'I thought it were the devil made your river, Annie,' Queenie cracked out, laughing.

'I think 'twere neither god nor devil made our river. 'Twere someone much older . . . the earth herself.'

'Aye,' Queenie nodded, her voice soft with reverence. 'The earth herself. That is something the gypsies have always known. Why else would we come?'

Minnie listened wide-eyed and silent to these two fierce women who feared neither god nor devil.

Queenie told of the great buildings she had seen being built close to the rivers to house the new spinning and weaving machines. They'd heard that someone had made a weaving loom that did not even need a man or woman to work it. Soon there'd be no work for weavers or spinners who did their work at home. Folk would have to get up early and set off to these great buildings, these enormous factories, to serve the new machines. Minnie looked over at Marcus the weaver who sat with his loom pulled up to the fire, close enough for some warmth and a little light. Though close enough, too, to hear what was being said, he never paused in his work, just smiled sadly, swaying gently in time to the clack of his treadles.

The gypsies had seen other things, dreadful things. Some of the places they'd travelled through were suffering from famine. What food there was had become expensive, so that the poorest people couldn't buy it.

Minnie listened, fascinated, promising herself silently that she would one day leave the cave and the small town which was all she knew, and go away to see for herself the amazing things that Queenie had seen. Perhaps she would go off with the gypsies. Yes, that's what she would do! She would hide herself in Queenie's wagon and only show herself when they'd gone many miles from Castleton.

The day that the gypsies left was freezing cold and the top of Mam Tor, the mother mountain, was hidden in mist. Minnie decided that she'd stow away with Queenie another year. She'd put up with the dreary round of work and the dampness of the cave a little longer to stay by the fireside and her sisters' warm bed.

# *Chapter Five*

At last, sharp spring sunlight came creeping into the cave. Thin pointers of dust-filled light pierced the dark corners of the underground village. Fetching the firewood was a pleasure, and Minnie went even more eagerly, glad of a good excuse to get into the warm sunlight. The younger children were sent out to take the pigs to graze.

Easter came and the children were given a holiday from their work. They went rushing around the village, searching for bottles which they scrubbed and cleaned. When all the containers were ready, they climbed the hillside beneath the castle to fill them with clear, cold water from Russet Well. Then there was the fuss and excitement of "the shaking". Each door in the village must be knocked on as the children begged little bits of liquorice and sugar to add to their bottles. Slowly the mixtures got stronger and sweeter. The bottles were shaken vigorously all the time, and even taken into the church on Easter Sunday, ready for the delicious drinking which happened when the service was over.

Minnie looked forward to the end of May for it was then that the celebration of the Castleton Garland took place. The Whittingham boys were already practising their dance steps with solemn concentration on the ropewalk below, while Minnie and Sally smirked and giggled.

The day before the ceremony saw the whole village humming with busyness. A huge wicker beehive was built and decorated with flowers that the children had gathered. There were bluebells, red campions and oak leaves, all tied and woven into the wickerwork with the greatest of care. This was the Garland, the very centre of the ceremony, ready to be placed over the head and shoulders of the Garland King.

Village women were engaged in a frantic session of brewing and baking, for when the serious work was over, there would be joyful celebrations.

Folk were up early on Garland Day and dressed in their best. The King of the Day was in old-fashioned clothes of the type King Charles would have worn when he came back to England. He'd come to restore the monarchy, but he'd also restored the ancient customs that had cheered the lives of ordinary folk. It was a great honour to be the Garland King. He climbed onto the best and most valuable horse that the village could provide. Then slowly he processed through the village streets, stopping at each public house where the landlord presented him with a drink.

Minnie and Sally pushed forward through the quiet crowd to see the dancers who followed the King. They did not laugh now at the Whittingham boys who were dressed in criss-cross ribbons and carried staffs of oak decorated with flowers, for this was their moment. The intricate steps were all-important, they must be performed just right.

The slow-moving parade at last reached the church where the beehive-shaped Garland was removed from the head of the King and hauled on the end of a long rope up to the very top of the church tower. There was a moment of silence, almost a moment of sadness. All eyes looked up towards it. Minnie caught her breath.

She turned to look back towards that ever-watchful eye, the opening of the cave, and though she could not see it, the knowledge that it was there brought a gentle flood of warmth and strength. Was there magic in this ceremony? Was there magic in this place? There *was* magic in the depths of their wonderful cave, Minnie felt sure of that. Her grandmother had known it, and blessed her with a dreary job . . . but she'd also blessed her with strength to carry it out.

'She will carry a rope and walk for ever. She shall be a spinner.'

Suddenly there was a great clopping of heavy hooves and a loud cheer as the King turned his horse around and the dancers took their places behind him. The procession set off again, and the dancers hurled themselves into the wild, abandoned criss-cross steps. There was laughter now, and singing. Food and drinks were brought out from the cottages. Minnie felt that she might burst with energy and cheerfulness. This was the best bit and she was going to enjoy herself. Dancing began and everyone joined in. Even the old ones pranced up and down. Minnie looked for a partner and saw that Sally had grabbed Ben Whittingham; Netty was dancing with some young man whom Minnie didn't know, but who wore a fine jacket and breeches. A stranger, and yet not quite; there was something that she recognised about him. Then she realised! She did know him, but what on earth was he doing here on Garland Day? It was the man called Josh, the Sheffield doctor's manservant.

She went pushing through the crowd of dancers to get to him, cursing as a heavy woman trod on her toe, while someone else kicked her shin.

When she reached Netty and her partner, she thrust her arm through the young man's.

'What you doing here? Aren't you supposed to be with your master in Sheffield?'

'Let go of him, will you?' Netty looked cross for once.

But Josh turned round, smiling, and kissed the top of her head.

'I've walked from Sheffield to see your Garland. I'd heard about it but I'd never seen it. A grand do it is too.'

'Dance with me,' said Minnie.

'Nay,' said Netty. 'He's my partner. Find your own, miss.'

'I'll dance with you next.' Josh winked as he said it.

Minnie turned away and shoved past the couples, back to the tables, grumbling as she went.

'I saw him first,' she told herself. 'I saw him first outside our cave. He would never have gone in if it weren't for me.' Then she spied Ned Whittingham, raising a mug of ale to his lips. She grabbed the mug from him and took a good swig herself, then plonked it down on the nearest table.

'Tha's too little to be swigging at that, Minnie Dakin.'

'I'm big enough to do owt I want at the Garland,' she said.

Ned stared open-mouthed at her.

'Shut tha gob, Ned, and dance with me.'

Ned was too surprised to object and his mouth stretched into a wide smile as Minnie pulled him in amongst the mass of swirling dancers.

# Chapter Six

It was four weeks after Garland Day that Josh Eyre again made the journey to Castleton. It was Sunday morning when he walked into the shade of the cavern and the good smell of mutton stew was drifting from the cottages. The ropewalks were empty and the winding wheels still while the workers sat on their doorsteps chatting, smoking pipes and drinking Dame Whittingham's ale.

Netty went running to hug Josh, her cheeks all pink with pleasure and shyness. She begged Annie to let him stay and to serve up the stew early, for it turned out that he'd set off at four o'clock that morning to walk from Sheffield and would have to be going back again in the afternoon, so that he could get back before dark, ready to serve the doctor his supper.

Minnie stared at him in disbelief. How could he walk that far and back in a day, just to spend an hour or two with their Netty? He'd used up his leave of one day a month on traipsing over the hills on those rough tracks. Of course he was a strong young man, though, you could see that. He had a comely face with a warm smile. She remembered thinking that right from the start, that day last autumn when she'd found him staring up at the cave entrance in horror.

'Fancy you coming all this way, Josh,' she said, jigging around him and Netty. 'Fancy you coming to a such a nasty hole as this. I can't think what can have made you want to come to such a horrid hole as this.'

'Leave him be, skinny Minnie,' Netty said. Josh reached out to tickle Minnie, chasing her round Netty while Sally fetched out the bowls and banged them down sullenly onto the table-top.

It was while they were eating their meal that Josh first began talking about he and Netty getting married. Mr Dakin looked surprised, but Josh quickly put before them all his plans. He'd hired himself to the doctor last Michaelmas, thinking that he'd get a chance to travel, live well and wear decent clothes, but the doctor had been hard to please, and Josh had travelled no further than Manchester. He planned to go back to his own home in Sheffield when he was released from the doctor's service next Michaelmas, and return to work with his father as a file cutter. There was room in their family cottage for him and Netty, and his father was begging him to come back, for with all the new trade and workshops that were being set up in Sheffield, the demand for files was greater than ever and Josh's father could sell his files as fast as he could produce them.

John Dakin nodded his head and listened to this determined young man so full of plans and energy.

'Aye, aye. If you can do it all as you say and make it all work out, then I cannot see why you and our Netty should not be wed.'

Annie was not so sure. Sheffield seemed far away to her. It was all right for a strong healthy young man to walk here in a day with naught to carry but himself, but for a woman who'd likely be hampered by little ones, the journey would not be easy.

'You'll not see us much, Netty,' she said. 'You'll be having your babies, and no mother there to help you. And besides,

I've heard them say that a file cutter's wife needs to be able
to help out . . . cut the files herself. File-cutting families work
together, and all you know is how to spin a rope yarn.'

But Netty could only laugh and cling onto Josh's arm, and
say that she could learn. Minnie sighed and grinned at the pair
of them. If she'd been old enough she'd have wanted to marry
him too.

It was early in October that Josh came to Castleton, released
from the doctor's service, ready to marry Netty. The sun shone
on the day of the wedding, and Minnie and Sally shared their
parents' bed, giving up their straw mattress to the couple. The
family went on singing and drinking inside the cave late into
the night, but they left Netty and Josh to have their wedding
night in peace. They'd to get up early next morning to travel
into Sheffield with the pack-horse train. Chapman Barber
made the regular journey over the hills, bringing with him the
ropemakers' hemp after it'd been beaten soft by the prisoners
in Manchester jail. The mules left the Castle Inn at daybreak,
and Netty and her baggage must be there if they wished for
the ride and the protection from robbers that the pack-horse
train might give.

Minnie could do nothing but grumble at being woken so
early. Sally's feet had been sticking into her back all night
and the unfamiliar sleeping arrangements had robbed them all
of their rest. It was only when Netty was at last perched on the
broad back of one of Chapman's mules, piled high behind
with clothes tied in bundles, that Minnie suddenly realised just
what she was losing. Sick panic arose. She was losing her best
and kindest sister, the one who saved her from Sally's sharp
tongue and her mother's demands.

'Netty,' she shouted, pulling at her ankle. Tears started up
quickly and rolled down her cheeks.

'Oh, lawks,' said Netty, her chin trembling, 'don't tha start that, our Minnie. Can't we be going, Chapman, or else I'll never do it.'

Chapman cried out, 'Get a move on, then!'

John Dakin laid a length of his best rope across his daughter's knee, folded and twisted and tied up with ribbon.

'Think of thee father when tha hangs up thee washing, lass.'

Tears poured down Netty's face.

Josh picked Minnie up and tried to hug her, but she pushed him away.

'I'll take good care of her, little Minnie,' said Josh. 'I promise you that.'

'You've stolen my sister,' she said and, as the lumbering train of mules clopped slowly away, nose to tail, with Josh walking beside Netty's mule, Minnie shouted after him, 'I'll never forgive you for that.'


Minnie spent the rest of the day working hard and fast, snapping at everyone, and it was only when she went to bed and found Sally already there and the mattress soaked with tears that she stopped to think that someone else might be feeling the same.

Sally's tears shocked her. Sally never cried. She'd been her usual sour self these last few weeks, perhaps a little quieter than usual. All the fuss had been for Netty and Minnie hadn't given Sally a thought.

'Sally. D-don't.' She wasn't used to saying anything kind to Sally. It was awkward even to try.

Sally rolled over, turning her back as Minnie lay down beside her. 'Don't cry, Sally. I don't like it if *you* cry. I want her, too. I can't think what it's going to be like without her.'

'Huh,' sobbed Sally. ''Tis not for that fat cow that I cry.'

'What then?'

There was silence while Minnie thought hard. Then she
turned towards Sally and put her hand around Sally's waist.

'I liked him, too,' she said. 'I saw him first. I spoke to him first.'

'Huh? You? Skinny Minnie?'

Sally giggled. She turned over and cuddled Minnie. They both laughed and giggled until at last they were worn out and fell asleep.

# Chapter Seven

Chapman Barber brought them messages and news of Netty from time to time as he passed through Castleton on his journeys from Sheffield to Manchester. It wasn't long before they heard that Netty was to have a child, and the following September Netty and Josh, with their tiny daughter bundled in soft cotton wrappings, came riding back to Castleton with the mules.

They stayed for one happy week which Minnie remembered for a long time. A week of hugging and chattering, of laughing and passing the baby from knee to knee around the fire while they ate warming stews from Annie's cooking pot.

Netty could not stop talking about the great size and bustle of Sheffield, and the good trade that Josh and his father were doing, though Josh's father had not been so well lately and Josh had needed to do most of the work. His mother was a skilled cutter, too, and she helped whenever she could.

'Even I am learning,' Netty told them. 'I was getting quite clever with it – wasn't I, Josh? – till I got so big with our little Marianne that I couldn't hold the chisel straight. Oh lawks, I wish you could see how they go on in Sheffield, though. The town is full of young lads that they call 'prentices. Such a sight they are, for when they're taken on, the mester buys 'em breeches. Decent leather if they're lucky, but how them lads do grow and those breeches have to last them whatever. I've never seen so many great lads all bursting out of their breeches.'

'That don't sound decent to me,' said Annie.

'Oh lawks, it ain't, is it Josh? They're running round with little aprons to cover themselves. Sometimes it's hessian breeches they get and that's just as bad, for as you know it stretches, and them as has hessian breeches has to hitch them all the time.'

'I wish I could see 'em,' said Minnie.

'You wouldn't if you saw Jack, our 'prentice,' said Netty. 'He's about as much use as I don't know what, but he's come to us when his father died. So we do the best we can.'

Soon the visitors had to go. Netty was afraid for her baby if they stayed any longer; they must get back before the cold weather came. Minnie begged them to take her back to Sheffield with them but Annie would not hear of such a thing, and there were more tears and clinging when they came to leave.

Minnie needed the cheerful memories of that week. They kept her going through the sadness and the difficulties which followed. Her oldest sister, Sarah, died giving birth to her tenth child the following winter. There were seven surviving little ones, and Annie took the oldest four to live in the cave with the ropemakers. Sally married Ben Whittingham and went to live in his cottage and work on one of the Whittingham ropewalks. Minnie found to her surprise that she missed the sharp, wicked gossips that they'd shared at night; they'd grown closer since Netty had gone. Now Minnie did her best to play big sister to poor Sarah's squabbling youngsters who invaded her bed once Sally had gone.

Netty couldn't make a visit the following year for she'd given birth to a boy who'd died after a few days of life, leaving her worn out and miserable. The next few years brought the happy news of two fine healthy boys, born with only twelve months between them. While Netty had her hands full with her three little ones, Annie was busy with Sarah's children, so the two families couldn't manage to see each other. Sally listened to the Sheffield news in silence. There was no sign of babies for her yet.

It was just before Easter in the year that Minnie was fourteen when Chapman Barber came into the cave. Minnie and her father had been up early that morning, taking the taut rope down from the tall pulley poles. They'd thrown off the heavy stones that weighted the rope and took the stretch from it, then they'd dipped it in the size trough. Minnie had become clever and capable at all these jobs, though she hadn't grown a great deal taller and sighed with despair at the skinniness of her arms. She'd even mastered the secret knots and twists for making whips, though it was more by her father's patience and her mother's faith than by her own hard work. Now Minnie was threatening the children and shouting at them to turn the wheel steady so that she could polish the finished rope with horsehair as they wound it onto the drums.

'Watch thyself, young Charlie,' she shouted. 'Keep your eyes on the wheel. How else can tha see what tha's up to?'

But Charlie could only stare past her at the pack-horseman, who'd never before left his mules behind at the Castle Inn and come right into the cave. Minnie turned around and jumped, not so much at the surprise of seeing him there as at the miserable look on his face.

'What is it? Is it our Netty?'

'It's thy father I should speak to, lass.'

'Father,' Minnie yelled, dropping the horsehair polisher. 'Charlie, run quick and fetch him. Oh no, she's never dead is she, like our Sarah?'

'No, she's not dead, but she's with child again, and she's sick.'

John Dakin came leaping down the terraced ropewalks.

'Your Netty is ailing, I fear,' said Chapman, 'and the family is in distress. Josh came up to see me and he begs that you will send young Minnie to help them out. The whole family is hard-pressed to make ends meet. The mester is dying, and the old woman has all she can do to nurse her husband and Netty, and feed the three little ones. Josh says he dare not stop his work for they've all got to eat. He says that Netty insists she can work, but she's not fit to be out of her bed and he thinks that she'll lose the little one and harm herself if they cannot find help.'

'I'll go, Father. I'll be glad to go.' Minnie's heart lifted at the thought of it, even though she knew she'd have to work. 'Chapman will take me, won't thee?'

'In four days I'll be back,' said Chapman, 'and setting off for Sheffield again. I'd take good care of her and see her safe to their cottage – if you can let her go, that is.'

John Dakin shook his head.

'Her mother will not have it.'


Annie refused at first.

'Not Minnie, not my Minnie. Not Grandma's special girl who's learnt the secret knots.'

But Minnie herself was determined. This was her chance. She'd see the world beyond her own valley.

'It cannot be Sally. She's already growing big with her first child, and it's taken her long enough. It must be me. I will not have our Netty die like Sarah did.'

Annie stood silent and miserable, but at last she nodded, unhappy, but seeing that there was no choice.

\*    \*    \*

The next three days were spent in preparation. Annie packed up soft sheep's wool blankets for the children, and into a pouch she crumbled dried burdock, comfrey and angelica, the strengthening herbs which Minnie could use to make healing possets for Netty and the old man.

It was only when the evening came and all her parcels were ready that Minnie was suddenly overwhelmed by fright and loneliness at the thought that she was leaving her cave. She crept down the ropewalks by herself and sat still and silent, close to the edge of the river. Just once, just once more before she went, she wanted to go through the tunnel into the huge darkness of the inner cavern. Just once more she wished to hear that strange pattering music from the constant sprinkle of water that fell in Roger Rain's House. She took the tallow candles, steel and flint from the cottage and then, without telling anyone, she unfastened the boat tub and stepped in, wobbling a little, and lowered herself into the straw at the bottom. She steadied one lighted candle on her chest while she pressed her other hand up on to the roof of the tunnel and nudged the tub along.

The scraping sound and shuddering of the tub told her that she'd got through, and she climbed out at the other end onto the gravelly beach. Feeling for the sloping cave side, she climbed until she found a small ledge, where she put down the tallow and left it burning while she stood back. It gave very little light in the great vast darkness of the cave, but gradually her eyes picked out the well-known shapes of the rocks and her ears accustomed themselves to the delicate music of Roger Rain's House.

Minnie caught her breath as she heard plashing from inside the tunnel and saw the glimmer of another candle reflected on the glistening rock walls. The dark water swirled white from the tunnel and her mother's anxious face appeared,

her gown soaked to the waist. When she saw her daughter
and her stillness as she crouched beneath the faint light, she
stopped. She watched her without speaking. Neither of them
knew for how long.

It was Minnie who suddenly shivered and broke the
silence.

'I'm going to miss my cave,' she said. 'I'd got so used to it
that I never stopped to wonder before. I never got to see what
a marvel it is. What is our cave? Where does it go to? Why
do the gypsies think it so special and come so regular every
Christmas?'

Annie went over to her and held her hand. She shook
her head.

'Aye, it is a mystery indeed, my girl, and I cannot give thee
a clear answer. All I know is that Queenie's gypsy gang have
been a'coming here for their Christmases more years than
anyone can recall. They'll tell you stories till kingdom come
about Old Nick and the robbers, but Queenie says as it's the
shepherd boy that got it right.

'To Peak's Hole come a-visiting,
A blessing on the land you'll bring.'

'The shepherd boy? That's always been my favourite
story.'

'Don't we know it. We wore ourselves out with telling it to
thee, when tha were a little 'un. But not Marcus, he always
had the patience to tell it thee over and over again. Well then?
What did the shepherd boy find in the cave?'

'Lovely fields of corn, and reapers gathering it in. Ah, yes:
a blessing on the land.'

'Now you've got it. It's an old belief. A visit to our cave
brings rain and sun, and golden corn. A blessing on the land.
I have got my own blessing to ask for today. Well, we've come

a-visiting, haven't we, you and me? Now let me think, how shall I say it? Ah yes, I've got it.'

Minnie pushed her arm through her mother's, smiling at her, waiting to hear what she'd say.

'To Peak's Hole we've come a-visiting,
A blessing on my daughter bring,
Keep her safe while she's away,
And bring her back, er . . . without delay.'

They both laughed at the last line, but their laughter echoed strangely around the cave and the deep tunnels. Minnie shivered.

'Oh, Mam, I need that blessing, for though I want to go, suddenly now, I'm feared.'

'Ah, my Minnie, you have naught to fear. You have the blessing of the cave on you, and don't forget that you have your grandmother's special blessing. You'll be back, my girl.'

'Oh, yes,' Minnie whispered. 'I'll be back, Mam.'

They stood together for a moment more, then Minnie shook
herself and became aware of her mother's dripping skirt.

'I've never known you to get your dress wet before. Not
without reason.'

Annie laughed. 'Reason enough, when my Minnie is going
far away. But get yourself back all dry, my lady. I can't be
sorting out your soaked petticoats before daybreak. I shall
have to wear my Sunday best now, to see my daughter on her
way to Sheffield.'

# Chapter Eight

A chilly wind blew down from Mam Tor as the first signs of daybreak lifted the darkness and the mules gathered, clattering their hooves and snorting, outside the Castle Inn.

Annie fussed about the cold and insisted that Minnie should have her best woollen shawl. Minnie herself was hot with the excitement of it, though she wrapped the shawl around her and promised to pass it on to Netty when she got to Sheffield.

'Little lass can ride up at the front on Chalky, if she likes, so long as she can stand the jingling of his bells,' said Chapman. 'Steady as you like is Chalky.'

Her father laughed as he threw her up to perch in front of the packs of wool that Chapman was carrying on to Sheffield from Manchester.

'See a fine lady on a white horse,' he said.
'Rings on her fingers and bells on her toes,
She shall have music wherever she goes.'

So Minnie rode out of Castleton at the front of the pack-horse train, feeling like a fine lady indeed, leading twenty mules loaded with panniers and baggage, with the bells on Chalky's collar jingling in her ears; leaving with scarcely a glance at the mother mountain, or the church tower where there'd soon be a new garland hanging, waving till she'd disappeared from sight. Her stomach pulled tight with pleasure as she got used to the steady lurching rhythm of the mule and her eyes were bright on the road ahead as they clattered along towards the village of Hope, which she knew well from market days. They crossed the River Derwent then went on to Hathersage, where Chapman brought her a mug of ale and bread and cheese from the inn. He and his lad then set about feeding the mules. They laughed at the stiff-legged walk that was all Minnie could manage when she'd bumped down from Chalky's back.

'Aye, tha's not used to it, lass, and tha's bound to feel it at first. It might be best if tha walks a bit now, for we've a steep pull up the hillside before we get to Ringinglow and the mules will have all on to get themselves and baggage up the slope.'

So, when the mules were once again muzzled and moving, Minnie set off walking beside Chalky's jingling harness, enjoying the blood racing around her body again with the stretching of her legs and the swinging of her arms.

They slowed as the hillside became more mountainous, and Minnie struggled to keep up with Chalky. The mules snorted and brayed, flicking their ears in protest and rolling their eyes. Despite their complaining, though, they followed Chalky's lead doggedly, while Chapman shouted at them from the back to get a move on. The climb became sharper, and Minnie was worn out. The mountainside began to feel threatening. There were few trees up on the higher ground and only heather and shale under foot, but the view was blocked in all directions by huge, strange-shaped rocks and boulders. Grand places for robbers to hide behind, thought Minnie. They could climb up easy onto those ledges and hide in the crevices, ready to jump down onto poor, weary travellers and threaten their lives.

A cold wind that carried a spitting of rain blew straight into their faces and the sky grew dark with grey clouds. Minnie walked close to Chalky's steaming side, wishing that she'd never left her home.

'Is tha feared, lass?' Chapman came up close behind her.

'Take hold of that rope that's tied to his bridle, and Chalky shall pull thee as well as his load.'

Minnie caught up the rope in her hands and clung to it, the familiar feel of it bringing comfort.

'Is this my father's rope, then?'

'It is that. And all the packthread that's on these loads. Who else's rope could I rely on but John Dakin's?'

So, stumbling and hopping to the side to avoid the clopping hooves, Minnie reached the end of the steep climb, grateful to Chalky for the extra pull. Once they were over the brink of the hill the sun came out, and the mules picked up speed. The land was still bare and rocky but flatter. The path ran on towards a bridge crossing a small brook in the distance.

'Upper Burbage bridge, then through White Moss. Ringing-low's not far now,' Chapman said, pointing ahead.

Minnie, still clutching onto the bridle rope, felt suddenly cheered. Her excitement returned and with it came new energy. Carry a rope and walk for ever. Wasn't that what her grandmother had said? It wasn't wrong to leave the cave after all. There was the rope in her hands, and she knew that she could walk forever. It was right, this travelling to Sheffield. It was meant to be.

'Tha can ride ag'in now, little lass,' Chapman called.

'Nay.' Minnie smiled at him. 'I can walk.'

# *Part Two: Into the City*

'The bounty of nature on Sheffield town smiles,
Yet could other trades work if we did not make files?'

Alexander Stephens, late eighteenth century.

# Chapter Nine

They could hear and see the wide turnpike road at Ringinglow long before they reached it. It was busy with traffic. Minnie had never seen a road like it. A fast four-in-hand went sweeping past, showering the slow-moving carts and wagons with dust. There was the jingling and braying of other pack-horse trains, and the shouting of the jaggers. Solitary chapmen with one or two tough skinny ponies ambled along, heavy laden.

Chapman Barber paid the toll, and Minnie climbed onto Chalky's back, not from weariness, but from wanting to get a good view of all that went on. She didn't want to do anything but look and listen, to stare at it all.

The road widened and curved round by a small group of cottages.

'Bents Green, this bend in the road,' Chapman said. He walked by Chalky's head, his hand resting on the mule's rough hairy neck. They'd not gone far when he clicked his tongue gently. 'Nah then, nah then.'

Chalky slowed his pace. Chapman said nothing more, but stared across the road at a gang of men, busy in the scrubby gorse-covered common land. They carried poles and lengths of string which they pulled straight and level, then hammered some kind of marking sticks into the ground. One man was scratching away at a roll of parchment he carried, making notes and drawing lines.

'What is it?' Minnie asked, sensing Chapman's disquiet.

'I don't like it. I don't like it at all. Them's Fairbanks' men that's a-doing all that measuring and marking.'

'But what's it mean? What is it that they're marking out?'

'Commons. Marking it into plots.'

'Ah.' Minnie caught her breath, for her parents had been speaking about it. They'd been worried. 'Are they marking it off, so as to close it up?'

'Aye, that's it. Fence it off and give it to those as has plenty of land already.'

'Mam was afraid of it happening, back at home. She said she couldn't see as how we'd manage to fatten the pig and keep the goats.'

'I'd heard it said that enclosures had been applied for round Sheffield, but this is the first I've seen of it coming about. There's going to be trouble before long.'

He set the mules moving and walked on, shaking his head. As they followed the road, they passed through tiny hamlets and villages. The traffic grew still faster and noisier. Steep hillsides and valleys, dotted with cottages, spread out before them, and here and there was a large, rich-looking house, and a church steeple . . . until at last the buildings seemed to gather together and fill the sides of a deep ravine where many valleys met. Workshops and chimneys threw trails of grey smoke up into the sky.

'There you are. There's Sheffield yonder,' Chapman showed her.

'It looks a grand, mucky place,' said Minnie.

They followed the road downhill and turned along the pack-horse road, Salter Lane.

''Tis the old salt route, this,' he told her. 'Nags like mine have been carrying salt down here since the days of the Romans. Wait while we reach the top of this hill then I'll

set them racking, and we'll be in Sheffield before you know. I
should climb down now, or else tha'll be shaken to pieces.'

Minnie was glad that she'd done as he said for when the last mule breasted the hill, Chapman shouted, 'Rack on, Chalky!' and the white mule broke into a fast rolling trot that almost turned into a gallop.

Minnie's hands flew up to protect her ears from the noise of the clattering hooves as the others followed Chalky. The baggage bobbed and lurched, held in place only by her father's strong packthread. It was deafening, but somehow wild and cheering; she sensed that the tough little animals were longing for the bran and fresh straw at the journey's end and would gladly run like this all the way to the inn. Minnie and Chapman had to move fast to keep up with them.

They racked their way down to the bottom of Salter Lane, then another lane called Sharrow. Chapman turned Chalky up a gentle slope of open land known as Sheffield Moor. They could see that the land here had been marked out for more enclosures, on the very edges of the city.

Minnie, perched high on Chalky's back once again, rode past new buildings and up to The Bird in Hand public house. This was the main stabling and stopping place for the pack-horse trains, but it was not quite the end of her journey. Minnie sat up there long after they'd stopped. Her neck ached from staring up at the buildings and the church. Crowds of shoving people filled the streets where the centre gutters were piled high with filth and rubbish; a rotting pile of stinking vegetables was heaped around the town stocks which faced the main gates of the churchyard.

Chapman chuckled at her amazement.

'Tha might well gawp, little lass. It's a sight to see and no mistaking, but tha' must shift thee'sen if I've to get thee down to Josh and Netty before dusk.'

So Minnie slithered down from the mule's back and wandered dazed and stiff-legged towards the market-place, while Chapman shouted orders to his lad and to the ostlers from The Bird in Hand. She stepped carefully around the rubbish and dung, watching with delight as a fine-dressed lady, followed by her maid, wobbled and teetered her way across the street. As she daintily lifted her skirts, slim white-stockinged ankles could be seen above soft leather slippers, then heavy iron pattens, keeping her feet high above the mess. Minnie put up her hand to cover her mouth, hiding her giggles.

'Now then,' shouted Chapman. 'Stop tha staring and let's get thee down to yonder nicker peckers.' He was leading Chalky, separated now from the rest, laden with Minnie's baggage and Annie's woollen rugs.

'Hasn't Chalky done enough today?' Minnie asked.

'Nay, this little racker can go for ever.'

Minnie threw her arm across the mule's neck and patted him. 'Like me,' she whispered. Then she frowned. 'What's nicker peckers?'

Chapman laughed. 'Has't never heard of it afore? Nicker peckers, nicker peckers, *tap, tap, tap*? Why it's what they call the file cutters. That's where we're off to . . . the nicker peckers' cottages, down by the river. Sheffield is full of nicker peckers and yellow bellies. Them's the grinders, yellow bellies.'

'Why are the file cutters called nicker peckers?'

'Ha! Tha shall know when we get there. I hope we find your Netty's getting over her sickness, though there's no chance for the old fella.'

'Is he so very old?'

'Why bless you, no. Not old for thee and me. He must be forty though. Old for a file cutter, that.'

'Forty?' Minnie was shocked. To her that was not so old at all. Though life in the cave was hard, those that managed to survive their childhood grew fit and healthy for the most. Grandma had been eighty when she'd died, and John Dakin was a fine strong man at sixty.

'Do all the file cutters die so young then?'

'Them as works long hours day in, day out — and which of them can afford not to do that these days? 'Tis the disease, you see. File cutters' disease, they call it. Tha'd best be prepared lass, for tha'll see it. Grey-coloured skin they get, and trouble with their stomach that will not go away. Then there's the blue line comes.'

'What's that?'

'Tha sees it when they smile. A blue line round the gums above the teeth. Them that has the blue line . . . for them it's bad.'

Minnie's face was grim. Her excitement turned to fear. It was not the old man she feared to see with a blue line around his teeth, but strong, handsome Josh.

'Why do they do such work, if it makes them so ill?'

'It's not easy to find work that doesn't make thee ill, lass. These new machines and working gear mean work, work and no stopping. The grinders' disease is maybe worse. Can't breathe, can't yellow bellies. Tha can hear a grinder coming from the wheezing and coughing that he does. It makes me think at times that I'm not so badly off with wicked robbers and freezing snow. At least I can breathe and walk.'

Minnie fell quiet as they passed the marshy area that Chapman called the Ponds, and walked down towards the file cutters' cottages which were huddled together for convenience close to the River Sheaf.

The light was fading as they got closer and Minnie heard the sounds, faint at first, then louder. It came from the backs of the cottages. *Tap, tap, tap.* Flickering lights in the lean-to sheds showed where the file cutters continued their work, candling into the night. *Tap, tap, tap.* It came from all around, as though rising up from the very earth; like the sound of a thousand woodpeckers at work in their trees.

Minnie smiled. 'I hear the nicker peckers,' she said.

# Chapter Ten

The cottage door was opened by a thin woman with smooth greying hair pulled tight back beneath a close-fitting blue cap. Minnie knew that she must be Josh's mother. Her wrap-over gown was made of strong blue-checked cotton, and a crisp blue apron was fastened round her narrow waist.

Minnie took a step back, closer to Chapman. She'd never seen any woman that looked so sharp in every way. Pale grey eyes, bony wrists, pointed elbows, thin tight lips without a trace of welcoming smile. For a moment Minnie thought of clinging to Chapman and begging him to take her home.

Josh's mother took a good look at Minnie, noticing every detail of her appearance: her dusty boots, the good woollen shawl, her uncovered curly hair. Not a flicker of friendliness changed the stern expression on her face, but she moved back and stood to one side.

'Tha sister's waiting for thee upstairs. Don't tha waken the little 'uns.'

Netty. That was why she'd come. Her own, kind Netty, whom she had not seen for so long, was upstairs, sick and needing her. But still it took a bit of courage for Minnie to step over the threshold, past that daunting woman. She squashed her curiosity about the insistent tapping that came from the back of the house, and went quietly up the stairs.

'Netty?' she called, near to tears.

'Hush!' A single candle burned in the small loft of the

cottage, and it took a moment or two for Minnie's eyes to get used to the gloom. She saw Netty over in the far corner, in a wooden box-bed, pulling herself up to sit. Minnie moved towards her, opening her eyes wide to see better, quickly taking in the sleeping children: two tiny boys curled together in a small box-bed, then another child – it must be the girl – rolling in her sleep, clutching some kind of doll. Carefully she crept past them, on tiptoes, then turned to hurl herself at Netty. But as she went, she caught her foot on something hard and wooden that took the skin off her ankle, and she skidded towards the bed with a thud.

'Ouch and dammit,' she yelled, rolling around on the floor beside Netty's bed.

'Oh, Minnie!' Netty burst into tears. The two little lads woke up, grabbed hold of each other and set up a great wailing. The girl sat up in her bed, still clutching the doll, yawning and rubbing her eyes. She threw back her blanket then, holding up the skirt of her nightshirt, she jigged up and down.

'Auntie Minnie. Auntie Minnie's come. Dance with me, Minnie. Me and my doll.'

The tapping from downstairs seemed to get louder. Minnie froze; it was not the tapping of the file cutting, but quick angry footsteps on the stairs. The old woman hissed and clicked her tongue in annoyance.

'How long did it take to settle them, Netty? How long? And now this. 'Shamed you should be, young woman. What a to-do.'

Minnie pulled herself up, rubbing her ankle, and plonked herself down on Netty's bed.

'Well, I'm sorry I'm sure, but you've got something sharp sticking out from your floor.'

She grabbed hold of the wooden object that had tripped her and pulled it closer to the light. The girl stopped her dancing and the two boys fell quiet. It was a wooden cradle. Minnie held it upside-down.

'I said it should be put away.' The old woman pressed her lips together. ''Tis bad luck to get out the cradle before the babe is ready to come.'

Netty's face was buried in her hands, her shoulders shook.

'Oh, Netty, I am so sorry. I never meant to cause such fuss and commotion,' Minnie said.

Netty looked up at them all through her fingers and, as she pulled her hands away, they saw that she was smiling. She was giggling.

'You were right, Mother. Put it away. I shouldn't be getting cradles out yet. And I've no need to worry, now that our Minnie's here.'

The two sisters hugged each other and cried, ignoring the older woman and the staring children. Then heavier footsteps on the stairs made them turn. Josh stood in the doorway, his arms held open wide.

'How's my saucy Minnie? Have you not a hug for your old Josh?'

Minnie flung herself at him and he swung her up into the air. 'Not-so-old Josh. Not yet.' She insisted.

She laughed at the strength in his arms and his bright eyes, but in the candlelight's gloom she could not tell the colour of his skin nor see if there could be a hint of blue in his smile.

Even though she was exhausted, Minnie could not sleep that night. She wasn't used to the creaking and rustling that came from the thatched roof of the cottage, nor to the cramped sleeping arrangements.

The worst thing of all was having to share a bed with Josh's mother, who'd inspected her for fleas before Minnie had been allowed to creep beneath the quilt. Minnie's patience had been tried to its limit and it was only beseeching looks from Netty that had kept her from remarking on the discomforts, and even dangers, of sleeping with someone whose elbows might spear you when she turned over in the night. No cuddling up to that!

As the first signs of dawn came creeping through the tiny oiled-paper window, Minnie crept from the bed, carefully so as not to disturb the sleeping woman with the thin, gaunt face wrapped closely in a night-cap. Gentle snoring made the tip of her nose quiver. Minnie shuddered. She'd rather snuggle in with Josh and Netty, but that wouldn't be allowed.

She crept over to their corner and stood quietly watching them in their sleep. The faint light turned their faces grey and Minnie could see that Netty, restless in her bed, had grown thin despite her swollen belly. She'd gained fine lines around her eyes and mouth, reminding Minnie, with a sudden catch of her breath, of their mother. She bent forward to examine Josh and smiled, for the peacefulness of sleep made him look young, as young as she'd ever seen him look. She had no need to worry about him.

She moved quietly towards the children and almost laughed to see the two boys curled together, the older one's arm flung protectively across his brother. But when she turned to look at the girl, she knew at once that this was where she'd prefer to sleep, though the small box-bed that Josh had built into the wall could never hold her as well.

This child was Marianne. This was the little one that they'd passed from knee to knee round Annie's cooking pot nearly six years ago when Netty had brought her baby to the cave. Minnie felt as though she was looking down on herself, but a good few years past. The brown curly hair spread wildly across the pillow was like her own, and there was something familiar about the faint smell that hung over the child. What was it? Minnie bent closer. It was the doll that Marianne clutched, warm with sleep; a strange doll. Minnie touched it carefully, so as not to waken the little girl. She smiled: a doll made of rope. The face was a flat coil which someone had stitched neatly together and the hair, another piece of rope stitched across the top and frayed at either end so that twisty rope curls hung down on either side of the blank face. The arms and legs were short pieces of rope, knotted at the ends for hands and feet. A tiny blue smock, made from the Dame's strong cotton pinafore stuff, covered the body, and the whole smelt gently of raw hemp and her father's size trough.

A creaking of the bed behind her made Minnie turn, to find Josh's mother dressing, fast and quietly, but keeping a sharp eye on her.

'Well,' she said in a hissing whisper. 'At least tha seems to be an early riser. Dress thee'sen and follow me down, and don't tha make a sound.'

Minnie pulled a face at the retreating back, but did as she was told. She'd come here to help Netty but she was quick enough to see that pleasing the Dame was the best way she could do that. So she followed her downstairs to the one room that was living room and kitchen, where the old man lay in a bed beside the fire. The 'prentice boy had already risen from his straw pallet on the other side of the hearth.

Minnie did her best to follow the instructions that were given; to rake the ash and carry it out to the midden; to fetch the coke and sticks and work the bellows; to feed the hens that scratched in the yard, and carry the waste-bucket to the pigsty at the back.

The work was no more than had been expected of her at home in the cave, but her back and legs still ached from the travelling and her eyes drooped for lack of sleep. Josh's mother moved quick and efficient round her fireplace, and by the time Josh came yawning and stretching down the stairs, they'd got the fire going and everything clean and sorted, with porridge (just as good as Annie's, Minnie had to admit) steaming in bowls on the table.

'You see, Mother,' said Josh. 'You'll find young Minnie a grand help.'

'Mebbe,' the Dame admitted, crisply, and went to feed her husband while Minnie and Josh sat down to their breakfast. Minnie turned her head away from the sight of the poor man who couldn't keep down the special thin porridge they'd made for him. He trembled and vomited while his wife fed him and wiped him patiently. How can she do that, Minnie wondered? How can she do that and then eat her own food? But Minnie saw that the Dame ate no breakfast herself, just set about washing the pots, tight-lipped as ever.

# Chapter Eleven

Once Josh and the apprentice boy were fed and off to their work in the shed at the back, Netty came shivering down the stairs with the children. Josh's mother shooed her back again.

'Here's tha chance to get thee'sen right and rested. Take it, Netty, for it seems that tha sister is some use after all.' She sniffed towards Minnie, not looking at her, and bustled the children along for their breakfast. Netty smiled her thanks to Minnie, then turned shakily back to her bed.

After they'd seen the children fed and dressed, Minnie crept out to the workshed at the back, wishing to see for herself what caused the nicker peckers' tapping. She found Josh hunched over a wooden cutting stock. He swung a heavy hammer up and down, hitting a fat, wedge-shaped chisel that he held with his left hand. Minnie moved forwards and screwed up her eyes to see better. The file was fixed to leather straps, with stirrups that hung down the side of the cutting stock. Josh had his feet hooked into the stirrups. As he pressed down on one side with his foot, the file moved along, so slightly. Each cut from the chisel fell fast and neat into the right place . . . *tap, tap, tapping* at each hammer fall.

The 'prentice boy was busy scouring the cut files with sand and dirty water. He stopped when he saw Minnie and grinned.

Josh, too, paused in his work.

'Now then, little sister. I cannot stop my work to tease you, for we're owing money all round.'

'I never thought tha could work so fast, Josh. The hammer hits at that chisel so fast, it fair makes me dizzy to watch.'

'Away with thee, lass, and see if tha can please my mother. She fears that tha's but another mouth for us to feed.'

Minnie heard a sharp tutting noise, and turned to see that Dame Eyre had followed her, with the children.

'Fetch the yokes, Jack, and take Minnie up to the well. Seeing as you're both going, you can fetch double the load. And take good notice of the way, girl, for you'll be making many a trip. If tha can do the job of fetching us water, then tha'll really be a help, and I shall be free to get some cutting done.'

Jack was a tall, fair-haired lad, about the same age as Minnie. He lifted down two wooden yokes, the sort they used in Castleton for carrying milk.

He swung them up onto his shoulder, looking at Minnie all the time in a way that she thought silly, and catching the edge of the table so that a jug and plates went skidding along. The children giggled and Dame Eyre raised her hand as though to clout his ear, but she just sighed and let her hand drop.

'Think what tha's doing, lad. Use thee eyes, can't tha. Now get those buckets will you, girl. On tha way and fetch the water as quick as you can.'

Still grinning and red in the face, Jack led the way out, up the street and round the corner, then up the hill to the well in the Ponds. Minnie followed him, cheerfully and briskly at first, then more slowly as they climbed the hill.

'Why come traipsing right up here to get the water when there's the river by the back door?'

'Eh?'

'Why not fetch the water from the river?'

Jack's eyes rolled up to the sky. 'Tha must be mad. Has't

seen river water? Them as drinks from t'river, them'll surely die.'

Minnie stared. 'But I thought they lived close by the river on purpose.'

'Oh, aye, but for the work. I fetch up river water for making the brine, and for damping the sand to scour the files. Then there's the water that I mix with lime to get rid of the salt afore the files are oiled. That's all river water that is, then we tip all't muck and waste from it back in't river again.'

Minnie shuddered and trudged on beside him. She'd always taken for granted their river in the cave, bursting clear and clean from beneath the rocks.

'Here it is,' said Jack, tripping over his boots in his hurry to get there. 'It's a good well this, grand water. Hey,' – he caught Minnie by the arm – 'back here! No pushing t'front. They'll pull out tha hair if tha does that.'

'What?' Minnie looked at the queue. Old women, young women, young lads and children all queued and pushed, watching each other with suspicion. There must have been thirty folk, with buckets and pitchers and jugs, all waiting their turn.

'Not too long,' said Jack. 'Usually worse than this.'

Minnie's shoulders drooped. 'How often do we come?'

Jack laughed. 'Not me now, *thee*. I'm just showing you t' way. Tha fetches it int' morning, then again int' evening, then sometimes at noon as well, depending on 'ow it goes and 'ow much you can carry. You'll be all right today 'cause we're fetching double.' He nodded his head at her, trying to please, but Minnie was not impressed. There were plenty of great gangling lads in the queue and a lot of little skinny ones, too. Why should others send their 'prentices to fetch the water, but not the Eyres?

'I don't see why you shouldn't fetch the water,' she told him. 'Look at some of these little lads that've come. They're all 'prentices, aren't they?'

'Oh, aye,' he said. 'They're 'prentices of a kind.'

'What d'you mean "of a kind"?'

'Well, look at 'em. Starving little kids they are. It's not the old 'prentice way, that. Not like Josh is with me. I knows when I'm lucky, though I do have to work hard. Only one 'prentice the Eyres have got, and that's me. Dame Eyre, she was my mam's friend, afore mam went and died, and though she's strict wi'me, she keeps a good table, I got to say that.'

He slapped his tight, round belly to prove it, and Minnie turned away, disgusted. Behind her were two skinny boys, both with large buckets to fill. They were pushed from all directions by people around, but they hadn't the strength to shove back.

'What did you say? What about these starving little kids?'

'Huh. Who cares? You and me's all right at the Eyres'.' He nudged her elbow in a way Minnie thought far too familiar, but she let it pass for she wanted to know more.

'Where do they come from? Where's their mams and dads?'

'Pauper kids they are. Come from the country, or even from London, sent off as 'prentices by the parishes. Saves on the Poor Money, see. It's the new way of going on. They don't just take on a few 'prentices, they take loads of 'em, and they keep 'em like animals and feed 'em less, but they teach 'em to turn out a lot of cheap goods. Make a lot of money like that.'

'Not files though. You can't make files like that. They'd just break, wouldn't they?'

'Who cares? They can make 'em so cheap, they'll sell anyway. It's only folk like Josh that's still struggling to do a proper job. I'm glad I'm not sharing my food with twenty more though, like them behind you.'

Minnie wondered if she could slip some of Dame Eyre's oatcake into her pockets next time she came.

It seemed a weary wait, but at last they got close to the front of the queue and Minnie pushed their bucket forward.

'Get back, Miss Push-to-Front,' said the fat woman before them. She had another bucket to fill and elbowed Minnie away, who fell back and trod on Jack's toe. A great commotion followed, for everyone lurched back onto their neighbour, and grumbled at each other.

'Give us your hand, little lass.' A tall, thickset man who spoke slow held out his huge hand to Minnie. He pulled her to her feet.

'Leave her be, John,' the fat woman snapped at him. 'Pick up tha buckets and follow me.'

The man turned and raised to his shoulders the most enormous pitcher that Minnie had seen. He followed the woman obediently, like a child.

'Come on then, get on with it. Our turn now.' Jack pushed the bucket into place, but Minnie turned to stare after the big man.

'That's John Bennet,' Jack said. 'Take no notice of him. He's daft, he is. Dame Furniss's apprentice, so they call him. He must be all of twenty-five, he's been 'prenticed for ten year or more and still not made a journeyman.'

'He's strong,' said Minnie, 'and he's no more daft than thee.'

Minnie spent the rest of the day running back and forth to Dame Eyre's orders, seeing to the children, carrying drinks to the sick man, cooking and cleaning, and keeping the fire going. At least she'd not been asked to make another visit to the well. By dusk she was fit to drop and ready for her bed, no matter whom she was to share it with. Josh's mother was pulling out the spinning wheel, moving it towards the fireside and asking her if she could spin a decent thread. Minnie was torn between weariness and fury at the insult of anyone asking her, a ropemaker's daughter, if she could spin, when they heard thumping and crying coming from upstairs.

'Never mind the spinning. Go up and help tha sister with that child. 'Tis Marianne again, she will not sleep. Both the lads settle down like lambs, but not that one. She's wearing Netty out again.'

Minnie went willingly upstairs; she'd rather tackle a naughty child than be starting to spin. She went over to the box-bed where Netty was sitting near to tears while Marianne swung her legs defiantly over the side.

'You get to bed, Netty. I'll see to this one.'

She snatched the rope doll from the astonished child's arms. Marianne at once set up a great wail.

Minnie held the doll up to Netty. 'Is this father's rope?'

Netty nodded, unsure of Minnie's idea of help.

'Shut tha noise, Marianne, and I'll tell you where Rope Dolly came from.'

Marianne closed her mouth in surprise. 'She's mine,' she said.

'Yours now, but I know where Rope Dolly used to live.'

'Where?'

'Lie down and cover yourself, and I will tell you all about it. That's it, snuggle down and close your eyes, then you will be able to see the great cave that Rope Dolly once lived in. A great cave with many rooms and tunnels that run deep into the earth. Once, many years ago, even before Rope Dolly was made, there was a young shepherd boy . . .'

Netty lay back in the big bed in the corner, a smile on her lips.

Marianne lay still and closed her eyes.

# Chapter Twelve

The days settled into a smooth rhythm of hard work. Once she knew what was expected of her, Minnie could do her jobs fast and efficiently, and she even earned some grudging praise from Dame Eyre. Netty recovered her health once she'd got the chance to rest and was soon up and about, organising the children, and baking and cleaning.

Marianne, carrying her own small pitcher, was sent with Minnie to help fetch the water, for Josh's mother insisted that they all learn to help.

Although Minnie got sick and weary of carrying back the heavy loads, there was some enjoyment to be had in the short bouts of freedom from Dame Eyre's watchful eyes.

'Go by Elsie Duckett's. Please, Minnie, please.'

Marianne pulled at Minnie's skirts, dragging her up the back street behind the well in the hopes of seeing Elsie Duckett's fat porker, the craftiest pig in Sheffield.

Like most folk, Elsie let her pig wander loose through the streets, gobbling up whatever edible waste he could find, stealing from kitchen doorways while the dames were busy, and generally growing fine and fat on others' food. Old Clarkey the pinder, whose job it was to round up stray pigs, particularly hated Elsie Duckett's pig and spent his days trying to catch him. But Elsie was as crafty as her pig. Whenever passing neighbours would call out, 'Clarkey's after tha pig ag'in, Elsie. Tha'll be paying fourpence to get him out of the pinfold,' she would pick up her tin bucket and bang it hard with a spoon so that Porker would hear the signal and head fast for home, knocking over anything or anyone that got in his way.

Marianne would scream with laughing at the sight of the pig racing through the streets and Clarkey, breathless and red-faced with rage, chasing after it, skidding through the rubbish and manure.

But this day was different. For once Elsie had her pig fastened by a rope to her doorway, then at the sound of a bell ringing up at the top of the street, she fetched a long-handled broom from her kitchen.

Marianne froze. She ran to Minnie, grabbing her arm. 'Water coming. Water's coming quick.'

Minnie stared at her stupidly. 'Water? What does tha mean? A water-seller?'

'No. Water coming down the streets.' Marianne tried to pull up Minnie's skirts, but was slapped and pushed away.

Minnie then saw that Elsie was hitching up *her* skirts and fastening them up at the back. The street was suddenly full of women with buckets and mops and brooms, pulling on old boots and fastening up their skirts.

'What's up, Elsie?' Minnie called.

Elsie looked at her, amazed.

'Does tha not know? Street-cleaning day.'

'Run back!' Marianne still tugged at her, but too late.

'It's here! It's here!' the shout went up. With a great whooshing sound, a green wave of foul-smelling water flooded the top of the street and pounded down towards them. Marianne leapt into Minnie's arms, her legs clinging safe and dry round her auntie's waist. Minnie could do nothing but groan and shudder at the smelly soaking that she got.

All around them was wild activity – shrieking, screaming,
dogs barking and the squealing of pigs. The piles of muck
and manure that filled the channel in the middle of the streets
were washed clear down the hill by the powerful tide of water.
The women washed and scrubbed, throwing buckets of water
at their houses, their windows and their children. Elsie took
her broom and scrubbed her pig.

Minnie returned to the Eyres', damp, uncomfortable and
stinking. Netty clapped her hands to her belly and laughed.

'Oh lor', I never said. Street-cleaning day.'

'No, you never,' said Minnie. 'Street-cleaning day! Whoever
heard of such a thing? Where does it come from, all that
water?'

'Barkers Pool, they call it,' the Dame told her. 'Used to be
lovely and clean, once. A big stone-built pool of drinking water
gathered from the top wells. It's got messed up now, all these
new folk flooding into Sheffield to find work . . . they abuse
it. 'Tis only fit for street-cleaning now.'

'Didn't tha hear the bell?' said Netty.

Despite Minnie's furious face, Netty couldn't stop the
giggles. Dame Eyre poured clean water into a bowl and
ordered Minnie to strip and change, but even her mouth
seemed to suffer from a slight twitching at the corners.

Josh began his working week on Monday, though many of the
workers called it St Monday and took it as a day of rest.
Minnie went along with Jack to fetch the blanks from the big
filesmiths' shops in the town centre. The work slowly built in
a crescendo until Friday and Saturday when everyone worked
at a frantic pace, for the finished jobs had to be taken back
and payment collected by Saturday night.

Minnie gaped at the sights that first Saturday night when
she'd gone into the town with Josh and Jack, helping to carry

the finished files all oiled and neatly wrapped. Payments were made in the public houses, but Josh made them go home dry-throated, even though Jack grumbled that they could do with a sup of ale. The town was riotous with folk singing and dancing, yelling at the fighting cocks and dogs ... and a great deal of arguing was going on over the cost of goods and

Explanation
1 Trinity Church
2 The New Church
3 The Towns Hall
4 The Shot House
5 The Shot House
6 Lades Bridge
7 The Separatists Chapel

To the worshipful the Master Wardens
Cutlers in Hallamshire in the County of
Town of SHEFFIELD is most humbly dedicated

FOUR F

money owed. The darkening streets were full of mesters and
dames, their way lit by young 'prentices carrying links and
rushlights. Those 'prentice lads who were let loose on the
town ran wild at the rare chance of freedom, playing daft
tricks and fighting. This was the big night out, this was what
they'd worked towards all week.

A noisy crowd gathered by a round-faced, broad-shouldered man who sat wrong-ways round on a donkey, his head facing its tail. He was singing, wagging his head and clapping his hands. Josh stopped to listen, an indulgent smile on his face.

''Tis Joe Mather,' he told Minnie. 'Him as used to be a nicker pecker – till he got squeezed out, that is. Now he's found a way of earning that he's more suited to, I think.'

Minnie pushed through the crowd, in closer to hear the singing. Joe had a deep, strong voice and kept a powerful rhythm, beating time on the donkey's rump, his broad shoulders swaying as he sang. Then those around him joined loudly in the chorus. Minnie listened carefully to catch the words.

'Wearied bones, despised and daunted,
Hungry guts and empty purse.
Hung with rags, by bailiffs haunted,
Prove the times grow worse and worse.'

Though the words were full of misery, they were sung with gusto and the performance ended in cheers and clapping.

'Well said, Joe!'

'Sing it again.'

'You tell 'em, Joe!'

'Sing us the file cutter's song!' Josh shouted.

Joe Mather nodded and lifted his hand for silence, then his deep voice swung into a song of sadness, telling of the difficulties of the file cutter's work.

Josh joined him for the last lines:

'I wield my six-pound hammer
Till I am grown round-backed.'

Then Joe held up a pile of broadsheets printed with the words that he'd been singing. Josh turned away.

'I wish that I could buy one,' he said, 'for Joe's the only one who speaks for us.'

They turned down Pudding Lane, past a miserable two-storeyed building that terrified Minnie. It was the debtors' jail. Dreadful sounds and disgusting smells drifted from the doorways, and from both the upper and lower windows arms were stretched, holding out tins to those who passed by. Despairing voices wailed and begged for pennies. Minnie shrank close to Josh as she glimpsed the snarling, toothless mouth of an old woman pressed flat against the window bars with her begging tin. Another tin swung on a rotting length of string from an upstairs window. Josh opened his pouch and brought out two small coins, placing one in each tin.

'Huh. That could have been a mug of ale for us,' Jack muttered.

'Aye,' said Josh, 'but see this purse? Most of it is owed to others. 'Twill not take much more, Jack, and I shall find myself in this rotten stinkhole.'

Minnie grabbed him by the arm and pulled him away.

'Come on home, Josh, I can't abide this place. It could never happen to you.'

'Don't tempt fate, young Minnie. It can happen to the best of us. Look at poor Joe Mather. He's seen the wrong side of those windows, and through no fault of his own but the one that I'm guilty of: too many mouths to feed.'

Netty grew bigger and Josh's fears became real. They were deep in debt. Still Josh insisted that they must have goat's milk for Netty and his father. They bought it from Nathan Woodhouse, who came into Sheffield from Crookes Moor on the outskirts, where he kept his goats.

Nathan had become a good friend, but the friendship grew strained when they owed him money, and he stopped calling at their door. They owed for rent and coal, and they'd run up an alehouse score though Josh had long since stopped sending out for ale to quench his thirst.

The hot weather came and with it, water shortages. Fetching water was harder than ever, and Minnie and Marianne learnt to creep fast and quiet to the front of the queue, ducking the slapping hands and dodging the trampling feet. They were lucky to return without a fight. Josh worked all hours, candling late into the night, but he could not seem to turn out enough finished files to catch up with their debts. The bailiffs came and slowly, stick by stick, all the decent furniture they had was taken.

Josh returned from delivering finished work one night to find Netty weeping. The bailiffs had taken the wooden cradle that he'd carved when Marianne was born. He rushed out after the men and begged them to give it back, but it ended in a brawl. Later, Josh came back to the house carried by his friends and drunk as never before.

# Chapter Thirteen

It was that night's drinking that brought the alehouse score up to forty shillings, and when the landlord heard whisperings of Josh owing money to others, he called in the debt. The constable came for Josh and took him before the magistrate.

Josh went off quiet and shamed. Minnie could hardly bear to see it. She wanted to run after them, to shout and argue that it wasn't fair, shout that Josh was an honest man and didn't deserve this. It would do no good though, she knew that, so she clamped her mouth shut and tried to copy the bitter silence of Netty and the Dame.

Jack watched it all wide-eyed. He whispered to Minnie that the magistrate would be old Niddledy Nod. He pulled a face and drew his finger across his throat.

'What?' Minnie cried out, horrified at the sign.

'Sets 'em all in the stocks, he does.'

Dame Eyre's hand slapped hard across Jack's face. 'Don't talk so stupid, lad.'

Minnie and Jack both gasped, shocked. The Dame had threatened it many a time, but had never actually hit him before.

'The magistrate is Vicar Wilkinson,' she said. ''Tis disrespectful to call him Niddledy Nod. The poor man can't help the twitch that he's got. He's not of my way of religion, but there's many that say he's fair. Someone has to try to keep order in Sheffield, and a hard task he's got. I'll have faith in the vicar, even though it's my own son I'm worried for. Now get to tha work, lad, and thee be off to fetch t'water, lass.'

They spent the day at their usual work, just as if Josh were there, though they missed the quick regular tapping from the workshed. Minnie grumbled that the awkward, uneven sounds which Jack produced got on her nerves.

Late in the afternoon, the Dame sent Jack up to the court to gather news of Josh. The three women waited together, restless and snapping at the children. Darkness fell and still there was no sign of Josh nor Jack. Netty was threatening to put on her shawl and walk up to the court herself when they heard stumbling footsteps and the creak of the workshed door.

Jack was hunched over the dying embers of the fire, holding out his hands for warmth, hands that could not seem to stop shaking.

'What is it, then? What's happened?' Netty demanded.

Jack shrank away from her. 'I don't like to tell thee, missus.'

'Oh, they've not set 'im in the stocks?'

Jack shook his head.

The Dame pressed her lips tight together. 'He's sent to the debtors' jail.'

'Aye.' Jack bellowed it. 'He's sent for three months, unless any will pay off his debt.' He hid his face in his arms.

'But in three months' time this child will 'ave been born, and how will we manage? We'll starve.' Helpless tears ran down Netty's face.

Minnie stared at her, stunned. She'd never for a moment thought that they'd do that to Josh. Even the Dame seemed lost for words, her face crumpled, and for one terrible moment Minnie feared that she might cry. She should have known better, though, for the Dame would never do that. Instead, she shook her head, shaking the weakness away.

'Off to tha bed, Netty. 'Twill not help our Josh if tha'rt sick again.'

She took Netty by the arm and led her into the cottage. Minnie followed awkwardly, finding her legs turned into wobbly sticks that threatened to snap.

Jack hovered behind them. As they began to climb the stairs, he made a strange mumbling sound which they could not hear clearly.

'Missus,' he said. 'Please, missus. Will I be sent off now, what with no Josh here?'

They all turned to look at him, his dirty face smudged clean and pale where he'd wiped away tears.

'Why no, of course tha'll stay with us,' said the Dame, almost fierce. 'Tha'll stay with us, come what may, Jack. Set out tha bed and get some sleep. Minnie must get to bed, too, for tomorrow both of you must start to fetch and carry to the debtors' jail. You must take him food and clothes and file blanks, for Josh must try to carry on his work inside that foul place, and we must rack our brains to see how we may manage. God forgive me,' she whispered to herself. 'I shall never speak up for that vicar again.'

Minnie woke early next morning and for one lovely moment she thought she must have dreamed that Josh was in prison, but the sight of Netty up and struggling clumsily to dress herself brought back reality.

'What are you up to?' Minnie asked. ''Tis me and Jack that's going up there, not you.'

'Oh, but I am,' said Netty, all trace of last night's weakness gone. 'There's things that must be done. He needs his food, and we must take kindling and clothes. Then we'll have to pay the garnish money, though I cannot think how.'

'What?' said Minnie, rolling herself out of bed. 'We must pay still more?'

'Aye. Rich debtors are kept in the high court rooms at the prison. They're not so bad, but you have to pay a lot. My poor Josh will have to be kept in the low court, that's the filthiest place, and we've even got to pay garnish money for that.'

'But we've got no money. What happens if we cannot pay?'

'Haven't you heard of the debtor's song? They sing it as each new prisoner is brought in. Well, not so much sing it as growl it. The Dame told me, it goes

'Welcome, welcome, brother debtor,
Pay your garnish, don't delay,
Or your coat will be in danger,
You must either strip or pay.'

'No!' Minnie was horrified.

Netty nodded. 'We must find some garnish money, or my Josh shall have no coat to his back.'

'Don't take on, Netty.' Minnie hugged her. 'Don't make thee'sen sick with it all. The Dame will get us through it, I think.'

'I don't know how, little sister. I don't know how.'


A tall man with the round shoulders of a file cutter was talking to the Dame when Minnie followed Netty downstairs. His face was grim, but Dame Eyre looked relieved. She held her hand out to Netty; in her palm lay twelve shilling pieces.

'Look, Netty. 'Tis Jem Kilner from the Filesmiths' Benefit Society. I always called our Josh names for bothering with that, for I never thought there could be any use in it.'

'Why bless you, sir,' said Netty. 'At least we can pay the garnish, and we need not starve.'

'Don't give me thanks, 'tis but your due. I wish we could

do more. There's plenty of our members right angry at this treatment of a good craftsman like Josh. He's not the only one by a long way.'

'Aye,' said the Dame. 'I never thought to hear myself agreeing with Joe Mather, but I start to understand him now.'

'Something must be done,' said Jem, 'but we cannot see what, or how to do it. It seems that every way our hands are tied.'

All their arguments could not put Netty off, and so she puffed her way up the hill to Pudding Lane jail, trailing behind Minnie, who was loaded with cutting gear, and Jack, who complained all the way at the weight of the lead resting-block.

It took a while for them to find Josh, such a wild, stinking jumble the whole place was, and they spent a good few of their precious pennies paying for the information.

They found him at last in the lower court, close to the file-cutting stocks where he'd asked to be, and shackled by the ankle. He was dirty and hollow-eyed but glad to see them, and he and Netty clung together and cried. Minnie and Jack stood by awkwardly, looking hopelessly for space to stack Josh's food and file blanks in safety. So cramped and crowded it was, that Minnie could scarce stand still without being shoved and grumbled at from all directions. She was desperate to relieve the aching in her arms from carrying Josh's hammer and chisel and she longed to clamp her hands around her nose, for the smells of miserable humanity were worse than she'd imagined.

Josh gently pushed Netty away from him and held her at arm's length.

'Tha must never come here again.'

Netty shook with sobbing.

Josh turned to Minnie. 'Thank you, little sister,' he said, kissing the top of her head. 'Tha's brought what I need. Now I can set about my work.'

He took the stuff they'd brought and stashed it as best he could behind the stocks. A skinny hand reached out at once for the bread. Josh grabbed a loaf and thrust it inside his shirt, then threw the rest towards the beseeching hands.

He took hold of Netty by the shoulders.

'Never come here again,' he said with anger. 'Promise me.'

This time Netty nodded her head, but she couldn't say the words.

'Get thee'sen off now. Minnie, take her home.'

Minnie somehow pulled her sister away and back through the dreadful crowd, leaving Jack to help Josh with his work and gather up the finished files, for anything would be seized upon and stolen if it were left for a moment, such was the desperation there.

The next weeks were harder than any that had gone before. Each morning Minnie and Jack toiled up the hill to the jail, fetching and carrying whatever was needed. Jack complained bitterly that he might as well be in prison himself, but Minnie told him smartly to hold his tongue and be grateful that he came back to the Eyres' cottage each night.

'They've stood by thee, daft 'prentice boy. Cannot tha stand by them?'

Jack hung his head.

'Aye,' he said.

As soon as Minnie had seen the two of them sorted for their work at the prison, she would go back to the cottage for Marianne and the buckets. The water-fetching job was worse than ever for the month was July and there'd been no rain for

weeks. It was mid-morning by the time they joined the queues
and the hot sun warmed the tempers of those who had to wait.
The 'prentice lads whined and fought like puppies, their lips
cracked and faces ripe with sores.

Minnie would often look out for John Bennet, the big man.
If he was there, he'd smile and wave, and let her into the queue
behind him. None dared to protest.

Sometimes, as they shuffled slowly towards the trickle of
precious water, Minnie would let her mind drift away from
the noise and squalor, remembering the cave and the clean
deep river. This was the growing time. The steep ravine that
led to the cave would be lush with the green leaves of trees
which grew out sideways – impossibly, it seemed – from the
rocky walls. Red campions and bluebells would be in flower,
clinging to the lower slopes, and the calls of rooks and magpies
would be echoing across the gap.

Late one Friday afternoon, though she ached to the bones
with the to-ing and fro-ing, Minnie persuaded the Dame to
let her walk up to The Bird in Hand inn, for she knew that
Chapman Barber would be fetching in his pack-horse train
there. She took Marianne, who was wild for every fresh scrap
of information she could glean about Rope Dolly's cave. They
stole a fine fresh carrot from beneath the snout of Elsie
Duckett's porker to take as a treat for Chalky.

Though Minnie was cheered by the sight of Chapman's
familiar face which linked this hard city with her home, it
was a sad exchange of information that took place. Minnie
related all that had happened with Josh, while Chapman had
to tell how Sally's baby had been born too soon and never
lived, and how it was only Annie's determined skill and care
that was slowly bringing Sally back to life.

# Chapter Fourteen

One hot Sunday morning, when Minnie returned to the cottage from fetching water, she heard slow uneven tapping coming from the workshed. She frowned, for it was unlike Jack to be trying to work on the one day that he was free and the Dame had gone off early to the Methodist Chapel. It was the one thing that took her from home, and she never missed.

The children had ceased their playing and stood round-eyed and quiet in the yard. Minnie stepped into the kitchen to find that Josh's father had pulled himself up from his pillow, distressed and shaking his head, though she could not understand the words he tried to speak. He pointed to the workshed and shook his head. The tapping stopped and a low moan followed. Minnie dumped the water down quick and hurried out to the shed. Jack was there, white-faced and scared, but it was not him at the cutting stocks. It was Netty, a hammer and chisel in her hands.

'I tried to stop 'er, honest I did. I said it weren't right.'

'What is it?' Minnie ran to her. 'What have you done?' She looked for blood on Netty's hands but could see none.

Netty's face was screwed up tight. Her hands gripped the tools rigidly.

Minnie hugged her, trying to give some comfort. 'What is it, Netty? Has't hurt thee'sen? There's no blood that I can see, love.'

'Aah,' Netty let out her breath and her face relaxed, leaving her pale and sweating. 'I fear I've set the little 'un off.'

'What? The baby?'

'Aye. Set it off coming far too early and not even a cradle to put it in now.'

Minnie stared hopeless and horrified.

'I'm feared I've harmed it to swing this damned hammer so,' said Netty. ''Twill not live, like our Sally's.' She gripped Minnie's shoulders tight, her body suddenly taut again.

'Sh-shall I run for t'old woman?' Jack stammered.

Minnie nodded frantically at him.

'I'll fetch her ... now.' Jack backed away from them, towards the cottage, but much to Minnie's relief the Dame herself then appeared in the doorway, still in her Sunday clothes, aware that something was wrong.

'Off to bed, my girl,' she said, firmly taking charge. She told Jack to sit downstairs with her husband and mind the children who just stared, distressed to see their mother bundled up the stairs, stiff with pain.

Between them, the Dame and Minnie managed to manouvre Netty onto the bed.

''Tis all wrong,' Netty sobbed. ''Tis not like the others. I've set little 'un off wrong, and it's coming too fast.'

The Dame knelt down beside the bed, leaning right over towards Netty so that her face, too, was on the pillow. Minnie didn't know whether to giggle or weep.

'Now see here,' said the Dame, forcing Netty to look at her. 'This child will come when it wants. There's many a fine baby comes both quick and early. You keep up your hopes, and with God's help we'll have a fine healthy child to show our Josh when he gets home.'

'Aye,' Netty nodded, biting her lips as she was drawn back into the pain.

There was no time to stop and worry now, with the baby coming so fast. Minnie rushed about trying to do as the Dame told her. She'd helped before, when Annie had attended a birthing, but there'd always been plenty of women around, fussing and elbowing in and handing out advice. This was different, frightening, with just the two of them and no time for fetching more help. This was her own Netty in great distress and losing blood. Dame Eyre gave her instructions clear and fast. Just as well, thought Minnie, for as soon as they'd got the bed covered, and the knife set in the fire, the baby was on its way with the head starting to show.

A low painful groan filled the house. This time, the sound had not come from Netty. The Dame looked at Minnie.

'Cans't manage for a moment, child?'

Then, without waiting for answer, she was off down the stairs to see to her husband. Netty gave a sharp growl of pain, and out into Minnie's hands slithered a small, struggling girl-child, spotted with blood and covered in the creamy sludge that protects the early-born.

Minnie stared, panic rising, her heart thudding fast. The arms waved and the tiny fists clenched, but mouth and nostrils were blocked. Minnie pulled up the hem of her soft cotton petticoat and, with her hands trembling, she gently wiped around the nose and mouth. Still the child failed to breathe. Minnie pinched the nostrils firmly till she could see that they were clear.

'Does it live? It makes no sound . . . it's as I feared.' Netty tried to heave herself up. The baby took a faltering breath . . . and howled. Netty flopped back onto the pillow, relieved. Minnie stooped to wipe around the eyes and was rewarded by a fierce glare, from eyes as steely-grey as her own.

The Dame's footsteps came hurrying upstairs at the sound of the child's cry.

'Tha's done well,' she said, when she'd examined the baby.
'Now fetch the knife, and thy father's twine, and we'll get this little 'un clean and wrapped.'

Minnie soothed the child while the Dame saw to Netty, and at last it seemed that their work was done. Netty had fallen into a deep sleep of exhaustion.

'You see to the mester now,' said Minnie. 'I can watch this little 'un.'

'Aye. You are right, Minnie.'

It was the first time that she'd called her by name. 'You are right. I must see to him now . . . for he died as the child was born.'

Minnie's mouth dropped open. She forgot to say that she was sorry.

'Like me,' she whispered, looking down at the baby, her arms tightening around it.

'What can tha mean, child?'

'Like me. Born in the moment of death.'

Minnie followed the Dame downstairs, carrying the baby still. She offered to help with the work of laying out, though she dreaded doing it.

'Nay. Sit thee'sen down and rock that little 'un, and watch the others while I get done. Fetch me that linen sash down from yon peg, Marianne. That's it, the one I fasten my gown with.'

Marianne fetched the sash, puzzled.

'Come here, Minnie. Put this over tha shoulder, good. Now wrap it snug round little 'un, then under your arm . . . like this, and I'll fasten it tight at the back. There now, you have your arms free and this child will feel as safe as if still in its mother's belly. Better than any cradle, that. Sit thee down and tell them one of tha tales. Aye, Jack can sit and listen, too. Tell about the cave. You know, the one they love to hear.'

'The shepherd boy,' said Marianne. 'The shepherd boy had lost his sheep . . .'

So Minnie settled to the story that she'd told so many times, rocking gently to soothe the baby, and her own fearful self, glancing over at the woman in the corner who went about her task quiet and dry-eyed.

# Chapter Fifteen

The Filesmiths' Benefit Society came to their aid once more and saved the mester from a pauper's burial. It was all done with respect and decency, just as the Dame wished it. Josh wept over his files in the debtors' jail with only Jack, who'd grown unusually quiet, to bear witness to his grief.

Although none of them would say it, the old man's death brought them some relief. The Dame was free to visit the jail and to do short spells of file cutting, all the while shouting to Minnie to wash the children and mix the brine and mash the tea.

Netty was weak, but she began the slow struggle back to strength and watched the tiny girl with wonder. Despite her size, the baby clung to life.

'Will tha give her a name, Minnie?' Netty begged. ''Twere thy hands that held her first.'

Minnie smiled with pleasure at being asked. She racked her brains, and thought of her grandmother, but then she thought of the poor mester who had just died.

'Call her Joanna, after Joseph Eyre,' she said.

The Dame took up her hand and pressed it.

'I thank thee kindly for that,' she said.

Minnie was back to the hated task of water carrying, dimly aware of something different in the city. There was little fighting now; quiet anger had taken its place. Minnie prayed for heavy rain, but she feared that what might come would be more like a storm of misery from folk who could bear no more.

It was very early one morning when Nathan Woodhouse came knocking on their door. Jack had spied him first and come flying in to tell the Dame.

''Tis Nathan come looking to call in his debt.'

Nathan hammered on the door again, but the Dame hesitated to answer it. Minnie turned sick in her stomach, for she knew that there was no money to pay him.

'Shall us hide?' said Jack. 'I don't think he spied me.'

'Nay,' the Dame shook her head. 'I'll not hide from Nathan. He's been a good friend.' She went to open the door.

'Will tha come in, Nathan,' she said, polite as ever, though her cheeks were red with shame.

Nathan came in, breathless and hurried.

'Don't tha fear, Dame Eyre,' he said. ''Tis not payment I'm after, at least it's not payment in money I'm asking of thee.'

'What then?' said the Dame, puzzled.

'Help is what we need. Thee'sens, as many folk as possible, to come out to Crookes Moor. We're determined to set our'sens in the way of the Commissioners' men. They have gone out this morning to fence off the common.'

They all stared in silence at Nathan. Minnie had heard of folk doing such things, but they'd always seemed far away and unreal, like something that happened in a story.

'Tha need not fear for the little 'uns, Dame Eyre, for we are determined that 'twill all be done peacable. 'Tis not a fight we're for. If we come in numbers, no need for that. We shall have a fine outing with picnicking and singing and dancing. All we shall do is get in their way.'

'I'll go,' said Jack.

'Aye . . . tha'd be good at it,' the Dame said.

'Tha might think it's not thy quarrel,' said Nathan, 'but there's many will be the worse for it. I'll not be fetching milk into town if my goats cannot feed on the common land. What work I'd turn my hand to, I don't know.'

'Aye, and we owe thee, Nathan, and have nowt to pay thee with.'

'I'd be glad for this help to take the place of payment, Dame Eyre. The Grinders' Society have given up work for the day. They're coming out to give us help. If we could get the file cutters to join us t'would be grand.'

Minnie's heart jumped with excitement at the thought of all those city folk leaving their work and surging out towards the commons. The Dame still hesitated. It was a hard thing for her to go against the law as passed by parliament. Never before had Minnie seen her undecided.

'I would not care so much,' said Nathan, 'if the land were to go where it's needed, but who is going to be gettin' it besides the Noble Duke, who owns all else, and those who work for him, and of course his friend the vicar.'

'What? The vicar's to gain more land?'

Nathan nodded.

The Dame's mouth dropped open, and Minnie knew that her mind was made up.

'Jack, tha must take a message to Jem Kilner and get him to fetch the file cutters and their families out to Crookes Moor. Minnie, run up to the jail and explain to our Josh. Netty and the child must stay here, and the two little lads, but we'll take Marianne and the rest of us will go.' The Dame unfastened her apron. 'Don't tha worry, Nathan, there'll be no file cutting done today.'

'I thank thee, Dame. 'Twill pay off all debts in my eyes.

Might tha have such a thing as a good strong rope to bring with thee?'

Minnie was out of breath before they'd even started. She'd been up to the jail and then to the well, but she was not the only one. The whole of the city was full of bustling folk, bright with purpose and energy, setting off for Hallam Commons.

It was almost noon by the time Minnie, Marianne, the Dame and Jack joined the crowd who were tramping through the town and along the bridle path to Crookes Moor. The Dame was laden with bread and cheese and water, and Minnie grumbled and rubbed her shoulders beneath the weight of her father's coiled rope.

'I might have known,' she muttered. 'Always the rope carrier.'

'What's tha on about now, lass?' the Dame asked, and Minnie found herself telling the story of her grandmother's death and the prediction she'd made. The Dame listened and smiled.

'Tha grandmother spoke true,' she said. 'Tha's a good rope carrier, and a grand strong lass to have around.'

Minnie strode on smiling, the warmth of the Dame's approval pushing her forward.

There was a great deal of shouting and angry fist-waving as they passed Broomhall, the stately house lived in by Vicar Wilkinson, who had disdained the vicarage overlooking the big church in the grimy centre of town.

Minnie had never seen so many people all hurrying along in one direction with one purpose in mind, but there was plenty of fun and laughing, and Joseph Mather's songs were bellowed out with gusto whenever spirits flagged.

Gangs of young 'prentices had been sent ahead as runners to spy on the Commissioners' men and carry messages so that the crowd could follow where they went. Already cheers and clapping could be heard as the upright poles for the fences were pulled out no sooner than they'd been hammered into place.

'There's the big man, the one we see at the well,' shouted Marianne, pulling away and wanting to run to him.

John Bennet followed a group of workers and, as they hammered a pole into place, he took hold with his bare hands and heaved it out, throwing it aside. Each time he did so, the folk around applauded as though it were a show. John bowed to them, excited and smiling. The Commissioners' workmen shouted at him and waved their fists, but none of them dared tackle a man of such obvious strength.

'They've no idea what a great daft thing he is,' said the Dame. 'That poor lad doesn't know what he's doing.'

'He's our friend,' said Marianne.

'Aye,' Minnie told the Dame. 'He saves us a place in the water queue.'

The Dame held Marianne's hand tightly and Minnie stuck close to them both. Only Jack plunged in amongst the crowd. He took the rope from Minnie, and made a slip knot in the end of it.

Two of the Commissioners' men were hammering poles in place. Jack ran fast with the rope and put it over the top of the pole they'd just set in place. Quick as a flash a gang of young lads had picked up the rope and heaved the pole out.

The two men were furious, but couldn't decide whether to chase the culprits or stick at their work. They snarled at each other, while the crowd chanted with wild joy:

'They hang the man and flog the woman
That steals the goose from off the common
But leave the greater criminal loose
That steals the common from the goose.'

'Where's our Jack now?' the Dame asked.

'He's there,' said Minnie, pointing.

Jack dived between the legs of one of the men and snatched away the hammer.

'Oh no,' said Minnie. 'Now he's for it.'

Jack threw the hammer deep into a gorse bush, then hurled himself down a sharp slope, head over heels.

'Jack, Jack,' shrieked Marianne. 'See him roll.'

The man followed him, hopelessly outpaced, then turned back frustrated and out of breath. Cursing and growling, he set about retrieving his hammer from deep inside the gorse.

'Fancy! Our Jack,' said the Dame, laughing in a way that Minnie couldn't believe. 'The little devil. Still, if anyone can create chaos it's our Jack, I should know. I never thought I'd live to be glad of it.'

'He's found what he's good at,' said Minnie. 'He's good at nowt else.'

'Aye, well,' said the Dame. 'Best let him run wild while he's got the chance. He's having to work hard enough with our Josh just now.'

The Commissioners' men struggled on for a while, shouting at the crowd and arguing with each other, but every way they turned, their tools were taken, the poles were pulled out and insults hurled. When one group of protesters wore themselves out with their tricks, a new group of 'prentices would take over with wild, fresh vigour. Well before dusk the Commissioners' men gave up their efforts, leaving the grass and gorse to the dancing crowds. They were chased back to their carts and wagons, so tired, so defeated that Minnie had a moment of sadness.

'I could almost feel sorry for them. Look at them run.'

'Aye,' said the Dame. 'Just working folk like the rest of us, trying to earn their way. Not really them that's to blame.'

Some of the young lads went daft with delight at their winning and ran around setting hayricks afire. The Dame called Jack away from them, insisting sternly that it was time to go. Minnie was glad; she was exhausted and longed for her bed. It was only the cheering sense of a small victory and Marianne's excited chatter that kept her going till they reached the cottage and the glad sight of a candle, which Netty had set in the window, burning in the dark.

# Chapter Sixteen

The next day was Saturday. Jack was sent up to the jail to help Josh and the Dame worked continuously at the file cutting, trying to make up for lost time.

That morning Minnie didn't mind going to fetch the water, for the town was alive with laughter and gossip and tales of Friday's doings.

But when Minnie went out in the evening, she found that the mood had changed. Fearful whisperings told of a meeting between the Duke of Norfolk's agent, the Master Cutler and Vicar Wilkinson. There'd been angry agreement between them that the enclosures must be enforced and those who objected brought to heel.

'They've sent some message off to the Home Office,' Dame Furniss told Minnie. 'They're asking for milit'y aid, so they say. You know what that means? Soldiers. Hundreds of 'em, riding into Sheffield. There'll be no stopping them fences going up then.'

Minnie reported it all to Dame Eyre but she refused to get angry or worried and just worked doggedly on.

'Well, we did what we thought right,' she said. 'It's all in the hands of God now. We must just go on working, and try to earn enough to buy our Josh out of that filthy hole.'

It was the first time ever that Minnie had known the Dame to miss her Sunday Methodists' meeting. She worked on at the file cutting all through the day. When Minnie took her

a candle as the light faded, she heard her muttering to the
rhythm of the hammer: 'He will forgive, he will forgive.'

Later that evening Dame Eyre sat counting pennies by
the fire.

'I think we can do it,' she said. 'If we can keep going at
this rate for the next three weeks, with me cutting and thee
to help, Minnie, I think we might make enough to have him
out. I've never seen our Josh look so worn and sick. I fear
for his health if he stays in that place the full three months.'

'Aye,' said Minnie. 'I doubt he gets much of the food we take;
those miserable snatchers around him get it. And the stink!'

The Dame shuddered. 'And the dust,' she said. 'All that lead
dust from the cutting block flying up into his face and mouth,
and he's no means of cleaning himself.'

'We'll do it,' said Minnie. 'We'll get him out. We'll work
like the very devil.'

The Dame frowned. 'With God's help, we'll work,' she
said.


So the family set themselves to work harder than ever. Netty
saw to the children's feeding and washing. Minnie ran back
and forth, and round in circles, fetching and carrying for the
Dame. She must have no need to stop work for anything other
than her own desperate weariness – which was all that
prevented her candling right through the night.

The three women were so busy that they took little notice of
the continuing rumours that filled the town. When the news
was out one Wednesday morning that a detachment of Light
Dragoons were coming from Nottingham, they shrugged their
shoulders and got on with their work. But that evening, when
Jack returned, he was wild with excitement.

'They've come, they've come,' he shouted. 'There's soldiers
on horses, with great swords, clatterin' through t'streets. And

all the town's out to see them. Like Saturday night, but worse. They're grumbling and shoving, and shouting that if soldiers be sent for, they'd better have summat to do.'

'Well, they're daft,' said the Dame, 'if they think they can do owt against soldiers.'

'They say,' said Jack, hopping from one foot to the other, punching the air with his fists to add drama, 'they say that if they can break open prisons in France, why should they not be doing it here?'

'What?' The Dame jumped up and grabbed Jack by the shoulders.

'It's true, missus. I had to fight my way through the crowds that was thick around Pudding Lane. They say they shall break open the debtors' jail.'

Netty was up and putting on her cloak.

'You're not going up there,' the Dame told her.

'That I am. 'Tis my Josh they may be letting out.'

The Dame sighed and nodded her head.

'Well, take Jack then, and thee go too, Minnie, for at least tha's strong. Keep tha sister away from the pushing and shoving, she's still weak from the birthing. Don't get thee'sens in the thick of it.'

It was a hot heavy night. They hadn't gone far before running feet and shouting could be heard coming from the centre of town.

Just as Jack had said, folk were crushed thick around the debtors' jail. From the outskirts of the crowd they could see rushlights being hurled about above the angry bellowing.

'Where's all these soldiers, then?' said Minnie.

'Gone to set up their tents and fill their bellies, so they say,' said Jack. 'Now's the time for trouble, for they don't know their way around the town yet.'

Netty tried to push between the solid backs of two men.
'Please,' she screamed. 'Please, my Josh's in that jail.'

'Stop tha shoving, woman. Haven't we all got folk in that damned place?'

Minnie pulled Netty back, fearful that the men would turn on her.

'What can we do?' Netty shrieked. 'We cannot get to him.'

'Here,' said Jack, 'shut tha noise, missus. Follow me and I'll show thee how.'

Minnie grabbed Netty by the hand and they set off quick and quiet now, circling round the edges of the crowd until they reached the front of the building. They were still no nearer to the main entrance.

'Now,' said Jack. 'We shall have to fight our way past a few of them, then nip down that first alleyway. It joins on to another narra' way that comes out by the main door.'

'Right,' said Minnie, and dived head downwards into the crowd, shoving and wriggling and trampling on any feet that got in her way, as she'd learned to do in the water queues. She pulled poor gasping Netty after her. They reached the alleyway and scuttled freely down it; it had somehow been overlooked by the angry gathering at the front of the building.

Jack led them into the next alleyway, round the back of the prison governor's house, and out towards the front again.

'Stay back,' he yelled at them, for the noise from the front of the jail was terrific. He stuck his head out from the end of the passageway, then threw up his hands to protect his face.

'They've smashed all t'doors and windows,' he said, 'and they be pulling t'prisoners out.'

Still waving his hand for them to keep back, he looked again, then turned his head towards the governor's house.

'Wait,' he yelled. 'They'm turning on't governor's house. Yeah! Smash his windows! Get 'im! Haul 'im out.'

There was the sound of shattering glass, and Minnie could wait no longer. She pushed past Jack, ducking beneath flailing fists and sticks, and round to the front of the jail.

Prisoners were being brought out through the main doors, some shrieking in a frenzy of excitement, others stunned and shivering. There was no sign of Josh who must still have been shackled to the cutting stocks. It wouldn't be easy to get him free. Minnie frantically pushed her way inside, past prisoners and liberators, Netty clinging tightly to her skirt all the while. They found Josh huddled fearfully in the corner along with other shackled men, unable to escape like the rest. Netty flung herself into his arms, while Minnie desperately looked around for help of some kind. What might happen to those left shackled when the soldiers came, as they surely would?

Then Minnie saw John Bennet. He stood head and shoulders above the crowd, laughing and excited, thinking it all a fine game. He held a great hammer in his hands.

'John! John!' Minnie shouted. He turned towards the familiar, shrill voice.

'Over here,' she yelled as loud as she could. 'Over here, John. Help!'

The big man made his way towards her. 'Now then, little lass.'

She grabbed his arm, and pointed to Josh. 'Can tha smash these chains, John, and let our Josh go free?'

'Aye. John can smash the chains,' he said, speaking slow as he always did. 'John can help thee, little lass.'

'Stand back, stand back,' shouted Minnie, as John raised the hammer above his head.

'Nay,' said Josh. 'Nay . . . I'm not sure as it's right to be freed this way.'

But the hammer fell, and Josh was free whether he wished it or not.

Netty pulled him to his feet and, one on each side, they steered Josh through the madness around them and out into the street. They left John Bennet to a clamour of voices begging him to set others free.

A clap of thunder echoed above the noise of the town, followed by the patter of heavy rain.

# Chapter Seventeen

The Dame was still tapping by the light of her candle when they returned, drenched and trailing water. She dropped her hammer and chisel into her lap and stared at Josh.

'Tha great daft lot. This is no good. Tha can't stay here, son.'

Josh gave a deep sigh and shook his head. Pale and bewildered, he lurched forward as though he was about to fall.

His mother was on her feet, hammer and chisel clanging to the floor.

'Son!' she cried. 'My Josh,' and caught him in her arms.

'We couldn't leave him there, Mother,' said Netty. 'Not when all the others had been let out. And I wished him to see the baby.'

The Dame shook her head, leading Josh into the cottage and making him sit down at the table like a child. Minnie and Netty followed.

'I don't know what's to be done for the best,' said the Dame, 'for the town is full of soldiers and there'll be houses searched for escaped prisoners. They'll be taking them back to the jail *and* keeping them there for longer, I dare say. Punishment will come for this.'

'No,' said Minnie. 'They'll not be searching houses tonight. The last we saw was the soldiers galloping up to the jail, but far too late, for most of the folk had gone by then, shouting that they were off to Broomhall.'

'What? Up to the vicar's place?'

'Aye. "To Broomhall," they were yelling and screaming.
"Burn the place down!" and off they went, leaving the soldiers
looking at the empty jail.'

'And the soldiers don't know Sheffield,' said Netty. ' "Where's
Broomhall?" they were asking. Folk were directing them every
which way but the right one. It'll take them all night to
find out.'

'And where's our Jack?' said the Dame.

They shook their heads. They hadn't seen Jack since they'd
lost him outside the jail.

'Hm. I daresay I know where he's likely to be.'

The Dame sent Netty and Josh off to bed, for they were
both done. They'd have to find somewhere to hide Josh in
the morning.

'And you, Minnie.' The Dame nodded towards the stairs.

'What will you do?' Minnie asked.

'I shall sit by this fire and rack my brains, and listen out for
soldiers or constables. Then at least we may get some warning.'

'I'll sit with thee,' said Minnie. 'For I swear I cannot sleep.'

It was early next morning, when the thick, black dark had
lifted to grey, that they heard the sound of running feet.
Minnie sat up with a jolt; she'd been drifting off to sleep
from sheer weariness.

There came the grating sound of the sneck on the workshed
door. The Dame took up her candle and carried it out across
the yard to the shed. Minnie followed. Jack was slumped in
front of the hearth, his usual place. They could almost have
thought he'd been there all night if it were not for the strange
stench that filled the shed.

'*Poof*, tha's brought a right stink in here with thee, Jack,'
Minnie told him. 'What's tha been up to?'

'Aye. What indeed?' the Dame insisted, holding the candle close to his face. 'How's this eye so red and swollen? And look at these breeches! A decent pair of hessian breeches we gave thee, lad. Just look at them: ripped, and stinking of filth and . . . is it burning?'

'Oh, missus. I'll tell thee . . . tell thee, missus, I will.'

Jack stammered and shook so that the Dame saw she'd get no sense out of him till he was calmed and fed.

'Stop,' she said. 'I want to know nothing till tha's all cleaned up. Get out of these things quick, lest the soldiers come knocking on our door. If they see the state of thee, they'll know tha's been up to mischief. Tha'll have to put on the old mester's clothes. I don't like it much, but it can't be helped.'

Jack didn't like it much either, but he was in no position to argue so he did as he was told and the Dame threw his filthy torn things on the fire. Minnie made him a bowl of porridge and thumped it down in front of him.

'Not that tha deserves owt.'

Then at last he began to tell what had happened; how he'd followed the angry crowd out to Broomhall as the soldiers were arriving at the jail.

'I never meant to go. I never meant it, missus. I just seemed to get carried along wi' them.'

'Huh,' said the Dame. 'You always never mean it, Jack, when there's trouble. Well? What happened then? Was the vicar at home?'

'Nay. He was out dining of course, growing fat and drunk on the backs of us.'

'Not fat,' the Dame insisted. 'Whatever you may say, you can't call him fat. The vicar is wiry and strong. They say he's a boxing man.'

Jack's shoulders drooped at the Dame's passionate honesty.

But then he grinned.

'We near burnt his house down, though. We set his hay-stacks alight and there was a right old blaze. Smashed his window, and wrecked this room that was filled with books.'

'You burnt his books! His library! Oh heavens, there'll be worse trouble coming for this, tha daft lad. I don't like to hear of them burning books.'

'We'd have burned the whole place down if it weren't for the rain coming on so heavy. And then the soldiers —'

'Yes. What then? What did they do?'

'We all ran off, missus. That's what. Ran off in all directions, and they chased us as best they could. There was folk clapped in chains, but not me. I'm fast.'

'Ah, I knew it. 'Twill be the worst for them that's caught. How many is it?'

'I couldn't say, but they got that big man that tha likes, Minnie. It took a great gang of them, but I saw them surround him and grab him. Then I ran.'

The Dame went quiet and thoughtful for a moment or two, then she got up, and put on her shawl.

'Keep alert, Minnie, while I'm out. I'm thinking I know where there'll be space for Josh to hide.'

She returned before long to find Minnie dishing out breakfast to Josh and Netty and the children. Marianne climbed and wriggled on her father's knee, wild with excitement to see him again. Josh, though, seemed to be struggling to eat the porridge they'd prepared for him.

The Dame stopped for a moment to look at them all. 'A fine sight you are. A fine sight to see, but you cannot go on like this, our Josh.'

'Aye, tha's right, Mother, but I cannot see clear what to do.'

'Dame Furniss will have thee round there. Tha can carry on with tha cutting in their shed, and tha can sleep in poor John Bennet's bed. He's built himself a great strong box-bed that has space beneath, if tha should need to hide. But they're not likely to trouble much round there, seeing as they've got poor John.'

Josh nodded. 'Tha's got it all worked out, Mother.'

'At least I can go round there to see thee,' Netty sadly agreed.

'Dame Furniss seems to think it's right. She's insisted that half of what tha cuts goes to her, mind. It seems a terrible thing to be making use of John Bennet's misfortune and I'm ashamed of it, but I cannot think what else to do.'

'John wouldn't mind,' said Minnie.

# Chapter Eighteen

The Dame had been right in her predictions of punishment: two more troops of dragoons arrived from York and Sheffield Town was indeed full of soldiers. Minnie's hopes for John Bennet were dashed, and in the early days of August he was sent off to York with five other men to stand trial.

As soon as word got round that the prisoners were being taken off through Attercliffe Common, Minnie had begged the Dame to let her go. She might be able to see John, and wish him well, or perhaps just the sight of a familiar friendly face might cheer him.

The Dame had insisted that Jack went with her for protection. Minnie had agreed, though what protection Jack offered she could not for the life of her see.

A big crowd had gathered, with only a few there to jeer at the prisoners. Relatives and friends followed the sad procession, wishing to go with them as far as they could, but Minnie turned back long before they'd left the outskirts of Sheffield. The sight of the big man heavily manacled, his face blank, uncomprehending, had shaken her to the core. She turned her misery on Jack. She hated his freedom and his clumsy attempts to make her laugh. She refused to speak to him for days.

In spite of the sadness and worry about those who were sent for trial, there was much secretive fun and rejoicing in the city.

Snatches of Joe Mather's songs were chanted in the streets, with another rhyme that came from no-one-knew-where.

Whenever the constables or soldiers passed through the streets, quiet chanting arose, then grew louder.

'They burnt his books,
And scared his rooks,
And set his stacks on fire.'

The week after John had been taken off to York, word came that soldiers and a constable were coming down towards the river, searching any houses that might be hiding the illegally released prisoners. The Dame looked anxious at the news.

'There's nowt to fear,' said Minnie. 'There's no sign of our Josh to be seen. And they've not bothered at all down Dame Furniss's way.'

''Tis Marianne I'm worried about,' said the Dame. 'The little lads are too small to say owt, but you know what a chatterbox that little lass is, and how excited she's been to see her dad. I don't know as she understands it right.'

Minnie nodded. 'Shall I take her out of the way?'

'Aye. That's a grand idea, Minnie. Take her up to the well and keep her away till dusk. And what about Jack, too? He's like to give them a mouthful of lip that'll fetch him another black eye, or worse. I know tha's angry with him, but take our Jack along as well, for he's nearly as daft with his talk as Marianne.'

Minnie sighed and agreed. 'We'll hunt for Elsie Duckett's pig.'

So Minnie found herself doing the usual trail up to the middle of town, smiling at Marianne but refusing to look at Jack. This treatment did not worry Jack in the least. He teased Marianne with his usual energy until she howled and stamped her feet and chased him up the street.

Minnie followed them slowly, heavy with misery as she thought about John Bennet. His trial would be taking place now, up there in York. Surely they'd set him free? The vicar had been paid a lot of money from the Town Trustees. Compensation they'd called it. Nobody had been hurt. Surely they'd let John go? He'd only done what his friends had asked, and Minnie herself had been one of those who'd asked.

She reached the corner by Elsie's house and looked round for Jack and Marianne. She could see no sign of them.

'Damn that lad,' she said. How was she supposed to know which way they'd gone?

Then she saw Jack, up near the corner of High Street. He came running down towards her, his mouth hanging open, his face bright red.

'Where's Marianne?' she shouted at him.

His mouth worked frantically and his eyes stared wildly at her. 'I never . . . I never thought. 'Twere meant in fun. Tha'll hit me, I know tha will.'

'What?' Minnie shrieked at him. 'Tell me, tha great stupid gawk. Has't lost her?'

Jack stared, quiet now and trembling. He shook his head, his eyes filled with tears. Minnie curled her fist up tight and held it to his throat.

'Tell me now, or I'll make thee sorry the soldiers never took thee.'

''Tis the rhyme,' said Jack. 'About the books, a-and the rooks.'

'Aye?' Minnie was puzzled. 'The one you taught her?'

'There were this man in't street. A . . . a gentleman . . . tall, wi' a big nose. I said, "Go and tell 'im the rhyme, Marianne."'

'So? She's but a little lass . . .'

Jack swallowed hard. ''Twere . . . 'twere the vicar hisself.'
Minnie stared, her own mouth dropped open.

''Twere just meant as a bit o'fun. I never thought. He . . .
he's called t'constable, to set her in't stocks.'

A fierce shower of blows rained down on Jack's head
from Minnie's fists. They landed fast and sharp.

A small crowd gathered, enjoying the show. At last her fury
died. Jack cringed on the dirty cobbles at her feet.

'I'll never forgive thee for this.' She spat at him, then
grabbed him by the collar, and hauled him off up the street.

As they turned the corner of High Street, Minnie closed her
eyes, and prayed that it was not true. But it was true. The
town constable was bending over at the stocks while Marianne
sat motionless on a stool, like a doll. As they got closer, Minnie
saw that the constable had pushed wooden wedges into the
holes around the child's ankles. She was too small to be fixed
into the stocks any other way.

A group of young 'prentices on the loose were gathering piles
of rotted vegetables, laughing and grinning with anticipation at
the unexpected lark of pelting a clean scrubbed girl-child.

'Now listen you here,' Minnie growled at Jack. 'You set
yourself in front of those stocks, and if so much as a speck of
that filth should touch Marianne . . .' She shoved him forward
and booted his backside.

Minnie marched up to the stocks and argued frantically
with the constable. He stood his ground, though, saying that
he didn't like it much himself, but the vicar was the magistrate
and whatever he ordered was done. Minnie looked round
angrily, ready to do battle with the vicar himself. 'And where
is our vicar now?' she demanded. The constable shrugged his
shoulders. 'Gone home for his tea, I dare say.'

Marianne, white-faced and puzzled, grabbed Minnie's

hand. 'Take me home, Minnie,' she said. 'I want Rope
Dolly, I want my mam.'

Minnie climbed onto the stool behind the child. She wrapped her arms around her, hugging her close.

'We'll sit here, my darling. We'll sit for a little while, and Minnie will tell you all your favourite stories. You will hear all about the robber chief, and about Rope Dolly's cave.'

'I wish I could go to Rope Dolly's cave,' whispered Marianne.

'Tha shall go there,' said Minnie. 'Tha shall go there, my darling. Minnie will take thee. I promise thee that.'

A small crowd began to gather for it was a rare sight to see: a young child fastened in the stocks and a blubbering lad setting himself in front, leaping about to catch the filth in order to protect her. An older lass sat rocking the child and calmly telling stories as though they were by their own fireside.

Whispers flew around, telling of the child's offence. A mood of sympathy grew and soon the muck-throwing apprentices were sent on their way with clouted ears to pay for their fun.

Elsie Duckett came past with her pig. She stopped by the stocks and stared fiercely at the scene.

'Dame Eyre shall hear of this.' She set off towards the Ponds.

It was late in the afternoon when the Dame came marching into the church square, bringing the constable with her. He hung his head, shamefaced, while the Dame poured a stream of quiet anger into his ears. The crowd around the stocks had grown, but the feeling had changed. They no longer gaped at the spectacle, but kept a silent watchful vigil.

The Dame picked up her grandchild as soon as Marianne was released and, without a word, she carried her off through the crowds. Minnie moved to follow them but stopped, remembering Jack, and turned back to look for him. He hovered behind the stocks, a foul-smelling figure of guilt and misery, not daring to follow. Minnie sighed. He had done as she'd told him. Not a speck, not a smudge of dirt had touched Marianne. He'd taken the lot.

'What's tha waiting for, Jack?' she called. 'Come on, and I'll help thee get washed.'

# Chapter Nineteen

The Dame strode ahead of them and by the time Minnie and Jack arrived back at the Eyres' house she had Marianne comfortable and warm, quietly nursing her rope doll by the fireside. Elsie Duckett, who'd stayed to watch the little 'uns, was just leaving with her pig tied to its rope. She pinched her nose as she passed Jack and hurried away.

'See,' said Minnie. 'Tha smells worse than her pig.'

The Dame told them that the soldiers had come. They had searched and found nothing, but now Netty had gone down to the Furniss's for there'd been word of the soldiers moving off in that direction.

'Does Netty know about . . .?' said Minnie, nodding towards Marianne.

'That she does not,' replied the Dame. 'She's worried enough about Josh without adding to it. We shall have to tell her, though, or she'll hear it from others soon enough. Now tha's got some explaining to do to me, lass. And thee, Jack, but tha'd best wash first, for tha's stinking worse than ever before.'

Minnie did her best to tell the Dame how it had all come about, though she dreaded her fury. The Dame was tight-lipped and silent as ever and Minnie knew she was angry. Luckily, the old woman's anger didn't seem to be directed towards her, or even Jack, but at the vicar and the constable, who could treat a child's prank so.

The Dame stood still for a moment, thinking, then she spoke.

'I'll say no more about it to thee, for I have news to tell that must make thee weep enough.'

'What now?'

The Dame sent Marianne to the table and made Minnie sit down in the fireside chair. She took her hand and held it tight.

'Now tha must be a good lass and stay calm, though I know tha was fond of him. Dame Furniss has had word that poor John Bennet is hanged at York. They've let the others go. I fear they've done it as an example. That poor daft lad has taken the blame for us all . . . That's right, there's no need to hold it back, love, have thee'sen a good cry while I feed these little 'uns.

Minnie did as she was told. All her anger, all her strength seemed drained in the flood of tears that overwhelmed her. Strangely, all she could think of was her strong stubborn father and how, despite the scorn of others, he'd always refused to twist the hangman's rope.

Jack tried awkwardly to speak to her, but the Dame called him over and told him to let her be. They busied themselves feeding the children, and when the workshed door sounded, the Dame looked over to see Minnie quiet and calm.

'That'll be Netty, I daresay. Slip out there with that candle, child, and tell her it all as best tha can.'

But Minnie didn't manage to get it said, for when she stepped through the workshed door, she was surprised to see that Josh was there, too, though he couldn't seem to stand straight and Netty supported him.

'What is it?' Minnie asked.

'He's sick, Minnie, that's what, and growing sicker down at that place. 'Twas that prison work, and now he works double for half the money. Show her, Josh.'

Josh shook his head. His cheeks were grey.

'Show her, Josh.' Netty repeated it sharp, then she pushed Josh roughly back against the wooden wall planks, pulling up his lips as though he were a horse.

Minnie gasped at the unexpected violence, but she stepped forward, holding up the candle. It was there. She could see it clear: a thin blue line around his gums. Netty released Josh's snarling lips, and hugged him to her.

'I'm sorry, love.'

Minnie stood frozen, still holding the candle high, watching them as they clung together. Just for a moment she could feel nothing but utter despair. She hated this cruel city. She hated this world . . . Hot fat dripped onto her hand, shocking and warming, and gradually the warmth spread up through her arms, her whole body. She was the ropemaker's daughter, the rope carrier. She could walk for ever, and never tire.

'We must go,' she said.

Netty stared. 'Where?'

'To Mother and Father. To the cave.'

'But how can we get there?' said Netty. 'I cannot leave the little 'uns, and Josh is too sick to walk far. I fear the soldiers might catch him on the way.'

The two sisters looked at each other, saying nothing, but both remembering the strong young Josh who'd once walked from Sheffield to Castleton in a morning.

There was a movement behind Minnie. The Dame was standing silently in the doorway. They did not know how long she had been there.

'The child is right. You must go, and you must go now. This town can do without thee for a while.'

'Aye, Mother,' said Josh. 'If only there was a way.'

'I know how,' said Minnie. Wild energy was flooding back

into her, her mind racing with the idea. 'Yes. I'm sure he'd help, and it's Friday night.'

They all frowned at her, puzzled.

'Where's my cloak?' She whirled around, racing into the cottage. 'There's no time to waste. Wrap up the children well, pack up what tha needs, Netty, and get us some food. I'll be back within the hour, and I pray that he'll not let us down.'

Minnie was back as she'd promised, leading Chalky, the white mule, followed by a grey, and Chapman Barber himself, come down willingly to the cottage to give his advice and set them on their way. Once Minnie had told him their troubles, he'd not hesitated, but fetched out Chalky from the stables and fastened the grey behind him.

'I know he's walked all day,' said Minnie.

'Don't tha recall what I once told thee, lass? This little racker will walk for ever. He's fed and had a few hours' rest. He'll take you well out of Sheffield tonight.'

The children were wide awake with excitement, and with Chapman's help and instructions they were all soon ready to leave. Netty sat astride Chalky with the tiny baby strapped warm and safe to her front, and the little lads settled within tapping distance in the baskets on either side. Josh had said he'd walk so that Minnie could ride, but he hadn't the strength to argue when Chapman and his mother lifted him onto the mule. He had managed a smile, though, when Minnie slapped her thighs to show him the strength of her legs. He was now set on the second mule with a great pile of baggage behind. They put Marianne up before him, clutching Rope Dolly to her chest, her strange frightening afternoon almost forgotten.

Chapman told them to stop at Ringinglow for the night. A cottager who knew him and his mules would give them shelter and stabling.

'Tha'll be safe enough from soldiers out there.'

Minnie clung to the Dame, clung to her thin spiky shoulders that once she'd hated so much.

'Won't tha come, too?' she whispered. 'Tha'd like our Annie, and she'd like thee.'

The Dame smiled and shook her head. For the first time, Minnie saw tears in her eyes.

'Tha's a grand little rope lass, and I'll miss thee sore, but me and Jack shall stay here. We're nicker peckers, we are, and we'll keep the work going so that Josh can return, if he's fit and Sheffield's safe for him. And there'll be something good coming from these terrible times, for Jem Kilner says how they're going to set up a society that'll link the different trades together. They can help each other then, and set about getting things right. Our Josh will want to be part of that, so get him well for us.'

Minnie linked her arm through Jack's. He looked pleased and awkward, and blushed deep crimson as she kissed his cheek.

Chapman took Chalky's leading-rope and put it into Minnie's hand. 'Set his nose up Salter Lane and he'll never falter, but lead thee to the cave. Tha'll be in Castleton tomorrow afternoon.'

Minnie took hold of the rope and sighed. 'Here we go. *Carry a rope and walk for ever.*' She whispered it in Chalky's ear as they moved off slowly, into the darkening dusk.

# *Epilogue*

Three women sat by the fire warming their hands, their faces lit by the flickering light of the flames. Netty was sixty-two. She was fat and round-faced, her cheeks pink and her silver hair shining golden in the firelight. She looked up into the darkness of the cave roof hanging above and around them like a giant cloak.

'Aye, it's been a grand day and no mistaking. Whoever would have thought it, her coming to visit us.'

'Now come on, Netty. 'Twere not really us she came visiting, 'twere the cave.' Sally, grey-haired, wiry and sharp as ever, insisted on the literal truth. 'Still,' she conceded, ''twere grand to get a chance to see her. Such a little lass she looks. Hard to believe that she's our queen.'

Minnie smiled silently, staring into the fire, unusually quiet. Her hair was grey and thinning but she was still a strong woman, with hands like leather.

'Our Minnie's awestruck with her moment of glory,' said Netty. 'Just fancy, Minnie, the famous ropemaker, demonstrating her craft to the young queen.'

Minnie suddenly laughed. 'I think she liked us. The way she asked us questions and listened all serious to what we said. They'd have pulled down our cottage and got rid of it, like all the others, if the children hadn't made such a fuss. They'd have made it all look neat if they'd had their way. They'd like to clear us out, too; awkward old women that we are, insisting on dying where we were born, messing up the place. Thank goodness the children stick up for us. Sally's lads wouldn't have us moved.

Sally laughed. 'Sally's lads? Netty's lads really.'

'No,' said Netty. 'Sally's lads is what they are. Ever since that day, so long ago, when we came struggling into Castleton in such a desperate plight. Eeh, dear! I thought you'd strangle me, the way you looked at first, and I knew it was hard. There was me turning up with all those little 'uns, and you just lost your child and no more like to come.'

'Aye,' Sally laughed. 'I could have strangled thee, it's true, but then . . . but then I saw the state of thee and I looked into the baskets and I saw those little lads.'

'We were worried for a moment,' said Minnie. 'The way thee looked at them, Sally, we thought tha'd eat them. But then before we knew, tha'd got them fed and tucked up warm in tha bed and . . . well, Sally's lads they've been, ever since.'

'I've been counting 'em all,' said Netty. 'Twenty-eight grandchildren we've got, and now there's the great grand-children coming. They'd never have survived if we hadn't shared them about. I just wish my Josh could be here to see them.'

'I wish he could, too,' said Minnie. 'But I'm glad he went back to Sheffield afore he died. He were that proud to belong to that society that they formed. Sheffield Society for Constitutional Information. What struggles they had.'

'Yes,' said Sally. 'He'd be glad to see the three of us still sat here in this cave refusing to budge. He'd be glad o' that. And tha's had enough little 'uns to satisfy us all, Netty.'

'And a good thing too,' Netty insisted. 'Marianne was always Minnie's special one, with her funny old rope dolly. And what with Minnie refusing all the best fellows. She's wedded to her craft all right, showing her knots and twists to the queen. Grandma knew what she said when she spoke those words. "Carry a rope and walk for ever. She shall be a spinner."'

# *Author's Note*

All the characters belonging to Minnie's family are fictional. However, the cave they lived in is the Peak Cavern in Castleton, Derbyshire. Ropemakers' families inhabited the cavern during the eighteenth century, and I have made the details of their lives as historically accurate as I can. The surnames Dakin, Whittingham, Marrison and Eyre are all associated with real ropemakers of Castleton.

Queen Victoria visited the cave in 1842. Three old woman were said to be the last inhabitants of the cave. They have been named as Sal Waugh, Betty Blowitt, and Mary (Nancy) Knight, who was the last to die in 1845.

Similarly, Josh's family of file cutters are all fictional characters, though I have tried to make the description of their lives realistic.

Joseph Mather, John Bennet and Vicar Wilkinson were all real people, and the events relating to them actually took place in Sheffield in 1791.

A story is told of a little girl who was set in the stocks. I cannot find any documentary proof that this happened, but it is often reported in history books referring to that period.

This is the way that R. E. Leader mentions it in his book, *Sheffield in the Eighteenth Century*:

'A little girl in the street was incited by some mischievous fellow to go up to a gentleman as he walked along and to say:

They burnt his books,
And scared his rooks,
And set his stacks on fire

— the well known doggerel relating to the rioters' attack on Broom Hall. The child innocently went in front of the gentleman, and, bobbing a curtsey, lisped out the lines.

"What my dear?" asked the vicar, for it was none other.

The child repeated it. "Yes, my dear," said he, "come along with me!" and, leading her by the hand, he took her to the church gates and had her put into the stocks.'

# List of Illustrations

# Select Bibliography

BAXTER, JOHN *Joseph Mather*, biographical notes, in the *Holberry Society Bulletin*, September 1978.

FERGUSON, JAMES *A description of the Devil's cave at Castletown*, from the *London Chronicle*, November 19th, 1772.

FIELD, E. *The Nicker Peckers. A brief history of file manufacture*, article in the *English Steel Corporation Review*, Spring 1967.

HALL, Dr J. C. *Trades of Sheffield as Influencing Life and Health. File Cutters and Grinders*, 1865.

HAMPSHIRE, GEORGE *The Sheffield Pioneers*, article in *The Sheffield Spectator*, June 1982.

LEADER, ROBERT E. *Sheffield in the Eighteenth Century*, 1905 (Sir W. C. Leng & Co. Ltd).

PAULUS, CAROLUS *The Manor and Parish of Eccleshall*, 1927.

RAWLINSON, R. *Twilight of a Ropewalk*, article in *Derbyshire Countryside*, April–May 1950.

WILSON, JOHN *The Songs of Joseph Mather*, 1862 (Pawson and Brailsford).

WOODALL, BRIAN *Peak Cavern: A Guide to this Famous Show-Cave; its Formation, History & Folklore*, 1976 (published by the author).